THE TELESCOPE

The story of the telescope is the story of astronomers who created their own "fingers to the sky." From Tycho Brahe in 1590 to the exciting discoveries of Kepler, Huygens and Halley, to the designers of the Mount Palomar Observatory, astronomers have been forced to invent their own instruments. One by one, each building on the genius that had gone before, the telescope makers extended man's knowledge out to the limits of the universe. An exciting chapter explains man-made satellites—how they work, what they will accomplish and how to track them with a telescope. A special feature is how to select and buy the best telescope for your purpose. Complete lists of organizations and publications, as well as dealers in telescopic materials, round out this all-inclusive book for those interested in knowing everything there is to know about THE TELESCOPE.

Books by Harry Edward Neal

Informational

COMMUNICATION
From Stone Age to Space Age

DIARY OF DEMOCRACY
The Story of Political Parties in America

FROM SPINNING WHEEL TO SPACECRAFT
The Story of the Industrial Revolution

MONEY

THE MYSTERY OF TIME

OIL

THE PROTECTORS
The Story of the Food and Drug Administration

SIX AGAINST CRIME
Treasury Agencies in Action

THE TELESCOPE

TREASURES BY THE MILLIONS
The Story of the Smithsonian Institution

Career

DISEASE DETECTIVES
Your Career in Medical Research

ENGINEERS UNLIMITED
Your Career in Engineering

NATURE'S GUARDIANS
Your Career in Conservation

SKYBLAZERS
Your Career in Aviation

YOUR CAREER IN ELECTRONICS

YOUR CAREER IN THE FOREIGN SERVICE

THE
TELESCOPE

BY HARRY EDWARD NEAL

*Illustrated with photographs
and line drawings*

JULIAN MESSNER
NEW YORK

$\overline{5}$
522.2
N

Published simultaneously in the United States and Canada by
Julian Messner, a division of Simon & Schuster, Inc.,
1 West 39th Street, New York, N.Y. 10018. All rights reserved.
Copyright, ©, 1958 by Harry Edward Neal

Tenth Printing, 1971

Printed in the United States of America
ISBN 0-671-32434-9 MCE
Library of Congress Catalog Card No. 58-6020

INTRODUCTION

The State of Kansas has a motto, *Ad astra per aspera*—
"To the stars, through difficulties."

This might well be the slogan of those pioneers who
invented and developed the telescope, and who are still
trying to improve upon it. The telescope as we know it
today survived a great many difficulties, some of which
would easily have discouraged most of us.

I have tried to tell the stories of many of the people
whose lives were completely dedicated to their work. I
have also tried to avoid the use of technical language that
might frighten away or confuse the average reader. There
are a few simple sketches and several photographs, merely
because I agree with the Chinese who said that one picture is worth ten thousand words.

The astronomer, professional and serious amateur, will
be aware that I have omitted the names of many persons
who played a part, small or large, in the development of
the telescope, and he also may feel that I have provided
too little information about others whose contributions
were of major importance to science. For this I am sorry,
but not all readers are astronomers, and wordage limits
made it quite impossible to include every name and every
biography. I have tried to include stories of the principal
actors in The Greatest Show in Sight—the fascinating
history of the telescope.

I could not have written as much as I did without a
great deal of invaluable help from a lot of generous
people, including Dr. John Hall, head of the Equatorial
Division, U.S. Naval Observatory, and his associate, Dr.

S. L. Sharpless; Mrs. Marjorie Clopine, Librarian, and Miss Helène Gingras, Assistant Librarian, U.S. Naval Observatory; Miss Grace C. Scholz, President of the Astronomical League, Alexandria, Va.; Mr. Charles DeVore, Assistant Technical Information Officer, Mr. Russell Sloanaker and Mr. Timothy P. McCullough, radio astronomers, all of the U.S. Naval Research Laboratory, Washington, D. C.; Mr. Armand Spitz, maker of the Spitz Planetarium and Coordinator of Visual Observations for the earth satellite program, Yorklyn, Delaware; Mr. Charles A. Federer, Editor, *Sky and Telescope* magazine, Cambridge, Mass.; Mr. J. L. Debes of the Eastman Kodak Company, Rochester, N. Y.; Mr. David L. Pierce and Mr. E. T. Decker of the Corning Glass Works, Corning, N. Y.; Mr. Albert V. Shatzel, Director of the Adler Planetarium, Chicago, Ill.; Miss Charlie M. Noble, Children's Museum, Fort Worth, Texas, and Mr. William G. Hassler, Director of the Museum; Mr. Philip Lichtman, young amateur astronomer, Washington, D. C.; Miss Margaret A. Mottier, Assistant Director of Research, Library Research Staff of the *Encyclopedia Britannica* (and her researchers!), Chicago, Ill.; Dr. Nicholas E. Wagman, Director, Allegheny Observatory of the University of Pittsburgh, Pittsburgh, Pa.; First Lieutenant James Perkins, U.S. Air Force, Washington, D. C.; Mr. Thomas E. Flanagan, Planning Officer, U.S. Information Agency, Washington, D. C.; Mr. J. F. Brandt, Manager, Consumer Products Sales Department, Bausch & Lomb Optical Company, Rochester, N. Y.; Mr. M. Livengood, Secretary, Lick Observatory, University of California, Mount Hamilton, Calif.; and my good friend, Col. Richard Hirsch, who made many helpful suggestions about source materials.

Perhaps my heartiest thanks should go to a lady whose

first name and present whereabouts I do not know. She is Miss Pumphrey (I hope I have spelled it correctly, ma'am!), and for a time she was the buyer of juvenile books for Ballantyne's Book Store in Washington. It was in that store that I was introduced to her at the time another book of mine was published, and it was then that she said to me, "Why don't you write a book about the telescope? A lot of young people come in here and ask about books on the telescope, but there isn't anything *readable* that seems to appeal to them. In fact, there isn't much of anything—period!"

There is now, Miss Pumphrey, wherever you are. And this is it.

HARRY EDWARD NEAL

Springfield, Maryland

CONTENTS

INTRODUCTION 5

1 THE TELESCOPE AND TYCHO 11

2 NO MAN IN THE MOON 20

3 THE GLASS EYE GROWS 32

4 THE MIRROR MEN 44

5 YANKEE GENIUS 63

6 A PLATE OF SKY 83

7 TOMB WITH A TELESCOPE 97

8 MAN ON A MOUNTAINTOP 109

9 THE SHINING GIANT 124

10 ENJOY THE TELESCOPE YOU HAVE 138

11 GET YOURSELF A TELESCOPE 154

12 DOWN HERE . . . AND OUT THERE 164

SOME OF THE WORLD'S LARGEST
TELESCOPES 175

SOME DEALERS IN TELESCOPES AND
ACCESSORIES 178

BIBLIOGRAPHY 181

INDEX 185

CHAPTER ONE

THE TELESCOPE AND TYCHO

Every day we go whizzing through space on the globe we call the earth. Above us are the heavens, and for centuries we have tried to fathom their mysteries. We are still trying. Many scientists are space detectives, searching the skies for clues to the past and the future, for in the vast reaches of the universe they believe that worlds similar to ours may be dead, or dying, or preparing to be born. By studying these celestial guinea pigs, perhaps they can learn exactly how our earth was formed—and how it may perish.

These scientists have already made many startling discoveries about the sun, the moon, the planets, the stars, the clouds of cosmic dust and gas that could engulf a thousand earths. Most of these former secrets were unveiled by the "private eye" we call the telescope, one of the greatest inventions of all time.

A telescope is simply a combination of polished glass disks, called lenses and mirrors, so arranged as to catch light from a bright object such as a star, and to concentrate a magnified image of the object in front of a human eye or a photographic plate. Basically there are two kinds of telescopes—refractors, which use a combination of lenses, and reflectors, which use both lenses and mirrors.

The telescope has helped to reveal the substances of which the sun and stars are made. It has shown us the sun's secret of atomic energy, and how we may use the sun as a source of power. The telescope has helped us to devise our calendars, to keep accurate time with our watches and clocks. As an aid to navigation it has brought countless ships to safe harbor. It has wiped many fears and superstitions out of our hearts and minds by showing us the truth about comets, meteors, eclipses, and other celestial fireworks that once terrified the world.

Thanks to the telescope, man has learned so much about outer space that he has succeeded in hurling man-made moons into it to seek new information. He is on the verge of building rocket ships which will carry human cargo to the real moon or to some other celestial body—but more plans and more telescopic observations are needed before a trip to the Great Unknown becomes a reality.

The telescope as we know it did not burst upon the world suddenly or ready-made. Man discovered glass, and found that glass would magnify, and then he made spectacles for people with poor eyesight, and finally a Dutch spectaclemaker's little boy discovered the secret of the telescope.

Gradually the value of this instrument was recognized by men of science who were hungry for more knowledge about the stars, and they sought to make it bigger, better, more powerful. It has taken centuries to bring the telescope to its present stage of development, yet few people know the drama, the joy, the heartbreak or the satisfaction that went into those years of trial and error, of failure and success.

This, then, is the story of the telescope and of the pioneers who worked with it to bring the stars to earth —truly the greatest show in sight.

The story has a short prologue about a scientist who never saw a telescope, who never even knew that such a device was possible, but whose contributions to astronomy paved the way for others and won him lasting fame. His name was Tycho Brahe (pronounced tie-ko bray).

Tycho was born December 14, 1546, at Knudstrup, near Lund, then a Danish province, now in Sweden. When he was only seven he studied Latin, and at thirteen he entered the University of Copenhagen to study law. In a class in astronomy he was told that there would be an eclipse of the sun at a certain hour on August 21, 1560. The eclipse took place at the very moment it had been predicted, and as he gazed in awe at the darkened sun, Tycho knew that he must pursue the study of the skies.

At sixteen he was sent to Leipzig to continue his law studies, but now the legal profession had no attraction for him because his eyes and his mind were among the stars. He saved his pocket money to buy books on astronomy, which he read in secret each night after others had retired.

One of his first purchases was a set of astronomical tables entitled *Tabulae Bergenses,* compiled by John

Stadius, which supposedly explained the positions and movements of celestial bodies. Tycho became so interested that he began to make mathematical calculations of his own, and he was soon surprised to find that his calculations did not agree with those in the published books. He reviewed his figures again and again, always with the same result. He was convinced that the published tables were wrong, and it was undoubtedly at this time that Tycho resolved to prepare information about the heavens which would be completely reliable. He began to study astronomy in earnest.

In 1565, when Tycho was nineteen, an uncle died in Knudstrup and Tycho returned home, but he soon departed for Germany to continue his work on the stars. In 1567, in Augsburg, with two fellow astronomers, John and Paul Hainzel, Tycho built a quadrant to measure altitudes of stars more accurately. A quadrant is a quarter of a circle—a device shaped like one fourth of a pie. The arc or curve between the two straight lines is divided into "minutes," a minute being one sixtieth part of a degree. Since there are 360 degrees in a full circle, and the quadrant represented one fourth of a circle, it was marked off in 90 degrees, and each degree was marked off in 60 minutes. By adjusting a movable arm, representing the radius of the arc, until it pointed to a certain star, one could measure the angle from the horizon to the star and thus compute its altitude.

But Tycho's quadrant was no portable instrument. It was about as high as a two-story house! The two straight pieces forming the angle were massive oak beams. Between them, like spokes, twelve other huge beams fanned out to support the arc, and these beams were reinforced with iron bands. Plates of shiny brass covered the arc, so that the plates might be carefully marked with 5,400 lines, or minutes.

Since it had to be used outdoors, a great oaken pillar, its base encased in iron, was set upright in the earth and held firm by stones and mortar. When the time came to move the giant quadrant, twenty strong men had to carry it to the pillar, to which it was then fastened. This tremendous measuring device, with which Tycho and the Hainzels carried on their studies of the stars, stood for some five years before it was blown down and smashed in a violent storm.

Armed with a great deal of knowledge and theories about the heavens, and with a few instruments he had bought in his travels, Tycho again went home in 1571 and persuaded another uncle, Steene Bille, to set up an observatory for him near Knudstrup, where Tycho proceeded to test some of his ideas.

He built instruments of his own, many on the gigantic scale of his oaken quadrant, and kept a careful record of all of his observations. On November 11, 1572, while gazing at the night sky, he noticed a strange star—a bright visitor which he had never seen before. This was of tremendous importance, because for centuries astronomers had identified the stars, and their charts failed to show one in the position described by Tycho. Some ridiculed Tycho at first, saying that he had found only a comet, but time proved that it was truly a nova, or "new" star, in the constellation of Cassiopeia, and even today some astronomers still call it "Tycho's Star."

In 1573, Tycho antagonized his noble family by marrying a peasant girl. Because his blue-blooded friends avoided him and his wife, Tycho took her on a trip to Germany, where he continued his astronomical studies. In 1575, when King Frederick II of Denmark, a friend of the Brahe family, asked Tycho to come home and take a position as Royal Astronomer, Tycho accepted—and thus began the building of one of the most unusual observatories in history.

The king gave Tycho the entire island of Hveen, or Hoene, some ten miles from Copenhagen, and agreed to provide money for an observatory, for instruments, and to pay Tycho a salary.

Tycho spent "nearly a ton of gold" to build the observatory, really a magnificent castle which he named Uraniborg, meaning "Fortress of the Heavens." In it he set up the instruments he had, and he built others —towering, massive frameworks of wood and metal which dwarfed Tycho and his assistants.

On the observatory walls he had artists paint huge murals, mostly showing Tycho with his slightly bulging stomach, his reddish beard and long mustache, which drooped like an inverted "U."

Landscaping was also important, and within the high walls surrounding the building Tycho designed beautiful gardens and lawns which made a picturebook setting for the castle. In addition, he erected four other buildings for some of his instruments, and he installed printing presses, carpenter shops and work areas for other trades. He soon built an additional, smaller, observatory which he called Stjerneborg, "Castle of the Stars."

In these surroundings Tycho Brahe lived and worked happily for about twenty years, making careful notes of his celestial observations, hoping one day to make an accurate measurement of the size of the entire universe.

When his friend, King Frederick II, died in 1588, Tycho's fortunes began to change for the worse. The new king, Christian IV, was not at first disagreeable, but there were many nobles who hated Tycho because of favors he had received at King Frederick's hands. These enemies slowly poisoned the mind of the new monarch against the Royal Astronomer, and within a few years Tycho's life became so unbearable that he could no longer do the work he loved. In 1596, the king ordered Tycho to leave Uraniborg, and placed others in charge of his giant instruments. In 1597, a heartbroken, weary Tycho gathered up his precious records, his personal belongings, and moved to Rostock, close to Hamburg, Germany.

There his reputation as a careful astronomer won him new life, for the emperor Rudolph II invited Tycho to work and teach in Prague, Bohemia (now Czechoslovakia). Tycho accepted, and immediately wrote to several young men asking if they would like to be his pupils and assistants. One of these was a teacher of mathematics at Graz, named Johann Kepler. Tycho's attention had been drawn to Kepler by

17

the latter's speeches about astronomy and about the orbits traveled by celestial bodies.

Kepler, a target of religious persecution, welcomed the opportunity and in 1599 joined Tycho in Prague, where they worked on a new set of astronomical tables which Tycho called the "Rudolphine Tables," in honor of the emperor. Tycho at last was fulfilling his youthful aim—to prepare tables showing the motions of the planets and the positions of the stars, based on fact instead of guesswork.

Tycho established the positions (latitude and longitude) of the brightest stars, 777 of which he listed in a catalog and marked on a globe. Day in, day out, for more than twenty years he also observed the planets and recorded their positions, believing that if he knew exactly how the planets moved, he might discover the reasons for such movement. He compiled hundreds of tables that he hoped could show where each planet would be twenty, thirty, fifty years ahead.

Unfortunately, Tycho fell critically ill before the project was completed. Anticipating that the end was near, he gave his priceless records to Johann Kepler and spent as much time as he could in telling Kepler how to continue the work after his death.

Tycho Brahe died October 24, 1601. We know today that he was probably the greatest and most accurate astronomer to make his observations and calculations with the unaided eye.

Replacing Tycho, Johann Kepler was appointed Imperial Astronomer. Born December 27, 1571, at Württemberg, Germany, Kepler was only four years old when he was stricken with smallpox, which left him with badly crippled hands and very poor eyesight. His father was a soldier of fortune, his mother an uneducated woman who was eventually arrested and imprisoned as a witch, although she was later acquitted of this charge.

Kepler had a long and brilliant career in astronomy. With Tycho's notes and his own observations he worked for twenty-three years to complete the Rudolphine Tables of Planetary Motions, which were finally published in 1627. His work led to the field of mathematics we now call *calculus*. Kepler was also probably the first science-fiction writer in history, for he once wrote a book called *The Somnium*, a story of a dream about a voyage to the moon.

Kepler later defined the laws of motion of the planets, thanks to Tycho's observations, and he also played a part in the development of the telescope.

It was about nine years after the death of Tycho Brahe when another famous man of science first looked through glass disks in a long tube and saw the moon at closer range than anyone had ever before dreamed of seeing it.

CHAPTER TWO

NO MAN IN
THE MOON

There is no evidence to prove who first learned that a piece of glass properly ground and polished, could magnify as well as or better than a globe filled with water. It is said that in 1255 an Italian named Salvino d'Armato degli Armati made pieces of glass which helped to strengthen the weak eyes of aged people.

In a book called *Opus Majus,* published in 1266, Roger Bacon, the English philosopher, told how one half of a glass sphere could be placed on paper with the flat side down to magnify writing.

Marco Polo said that during his travels in 1275 he saw the Chinese wearing glasses to improve their vision. In Europe, by 1280, small magnifying glasses were being made into spectacles to strengthen weak eyes. Such a glass was called a *lens,* the word being taken from *lentil,* because the lentil seed and the lens were so similar in shape.

Most spectacles were made only for old people who were either farsighted or nearsighted. Books were rare, and only the monks in the monasteries and a few of the nobles were able to read at all, so there was no reason to make glasses which would require fine adjustments to the eyes of the wearers. But after Johann Gutenberg invented printing with movable type in the middle of the fifteenth century, more books were printed and more people began to read. By the sixteenth century the wearing of glasses was common and there were many spectaclemakers throughout Europe, especially in France, Germany and Holland.

Evidence indicates that one of these, Hans Lippershey, or Lippersheim, of Middelburg, Holland, invented the telescope about 1608. If this version is true, then credit for the discovery should really go to Lippershey's son, who was playing with two of his father's spectacle lenses when he found "the big look." One lens was plano-concave, with one flat side and the other hollowed out like a saucer. The other lens was plano-convex, flat on one side and bulging on the other —just the opposite of the first.

The boy held the concave lens near one eye and the convex lens almost an arm's length away. Looking through both of them at a church steeple some distance down the street, he was surprised to see that a weather vane on top of the steeple seemed suddenly to be much larger and nearer than it was without the lenses. He ran into the shop.

"Papa!" he cried. "Papa, come and look!"

At first his father laughed because the boy was so excited, but in a few moments his son grew calmer and told how he had made the weather vane on the steeple come up the street and stand right in front of him.

Lippershey and his son went outdoors, where the spectaclemaker held the glasses as the boy had done.

Sure enough—the weather vane seemed much closer, much larger. Lippershey then mounted the two lenses on a board, in line with each other, thus making the first crude *refracting* telescope. (*Reflecting* telescopes came later).

He soon applied for a patent on the instrument, but the government refused to issue one, wanting to keep the discovery a secret for military reasons.

There are other tales about the origin of the telescope. One is that the secret was discovered by two brothers, Hans and Zacharias Janssen, spectacle-makers, also of Middelburg, and that they happened upon it by accident in much the same way as Lippershey did. Still another source claims the inventor was a Dutchman named James Metius, of Alkmaar.

The first telescopes were regarded by many people as toys, but government officials considered the instrument a valuable military weapon through which a general could watch his enemy at a safe distance—a wonderful way to spy upon a whole army without being seen! It was Galileo Galilei of Padua, in Italy, who showed the world that the telescope was more than a toy or a weapon of war.

Galileo is frequently credited with having invented the telescope. He himself admitted that it was invented by a Dutchman, but it is certainly true that Galileo was the first to demonstrate the tremendous value of the long glass eye to mankind—even though the wonders which he was the first to see in the unknown heavens brought him to the very brink of imprisonment and torture.

22

Galileo had a small body and a vast intellect, both of which his father wanted him to apply to the study of medicine. Galileo was born in Pisa, Italy, on February 14, 1564, where his father kept careful watch to see that the boy learned nothing whatever about mathematics. The father, Vincenzio Galilei, was himself an expert mathematician, and it may be that he looked upon a medical career as more profitable for his son than a lifetime of problems in arithmetic.

In 1581, when Galileo was seventeen, his father sent him to the University of Pisa to study medicine. In the school the boy was fascinated when he overheard other students discussing problems in geometry, and he asked all sorts of rapid-fire questions about numbers and equations. He wasted no time in seeking more information about mathematics, for this was a whole new world which Galileo enjoyed, a world he must explore. He had a long talk with his father, who yielded to his son's pleading and agreed that the boy could study mathematics and science instead of medicine.

Eight years later, in 1589, Galileo was appointed a Professor of Mathematics at the University of Pisa. In 1591 he was forced to resign because he disagreed with some of the theories of Aristotle, but the next year he was made Professor of Mathematics at the University of Padua.

In 1610, a report reached Galileo that a Dutchman had invented a "spyglass" which made distant objects seem near. Immediately Galileo determined to make such a glass himself.

"I prepared a tube," he wrote later, "at first of lead, in the ends of which I fitted two glass lenses, both plane (flat) on one side, but on the other side one spherically convex and the other concave."

It is said that the tube he used for his telescope was actually a leaden pipe from a church organ. Some say Galileo was the first to give the instrument the name of "telescope," from the Greek words *tele,* meaning "far off," and *skopein,* "to look." Others credit origin of the term to Johann Demisiani, who attended a banquet in Rome on April 14, 1611, where Galileo, as the guest of honor, exhibited his telescope and explained how it worked.

This first Galilean spyglass magnified objects only three times, but it was big enough to show Galileo that he had discovered a way to learn some of the secrets of the stars, the moon, the sun—the universe. He made a longer tube and larger lenses, which made objects eight times closer instead of three.

Word of his glass reached the doge, or chief magistrate of Venice, who invited Galileo to come to that city and show his telescope to the members of the Senate. Galileo accepted the invitation, and his instrument astonished all who looked through it.

"Many noblemen and senators, although of great age," he said later, "mounted the steps of the highest church towers at Venice in order to see sails and shipping that were so far off that it was two hours before they were seen steering full sail into the harbor without my spy-glass, for the effect of my instrument is such that it makes an object fifty miles off appear as large and near as if it were only five."

This telescope was only about twenty inches long. Galileo wanted to make one much larger, with which he could bring the heavens down to earth, so he presented this instrument to the doge and returned to Padua to start work on what was then a giant telescope. He made a tube 49 inches long, with an eyepiece 1¾ inches in diameter, which brought objects thirty-two times closer! On the day he finished it he was impatient for darkness to come so that he might have the very first look at the stars brought nearer the earth than ever before.

Like the others made by Galileo, this telescope was very simple in design. It was made with two lenses, one concave, the other convex. When the image of the moon (or other stellar object) met the convex lens, the light from the object was concentrated and brought to a very small size in front of the concave lens through which the observer looked. The image was magnified by the lenses, but there was one trouble. The concave lens had a diameter greater than that of the eye, and only a part of the concave lens was effective, because any of the light which was outside the diameter of the eye itself was wasted (Figure 1).

Also, Galileo's telescope had a fault which was later to be found in other refractors with simple lenses—a fault called "chromatic aberration." In chromatic aberration, all the light from the sun or stars passing through an ordinary convex lens does not focus to one point, because this light is really a combination of all colors, and different colors are bent at different angles as they pass through a curved lens. The result is that the image in a telescope like Galileo's is surrounded by a halo of various colors which make it difficult for the observer to see the image properly.

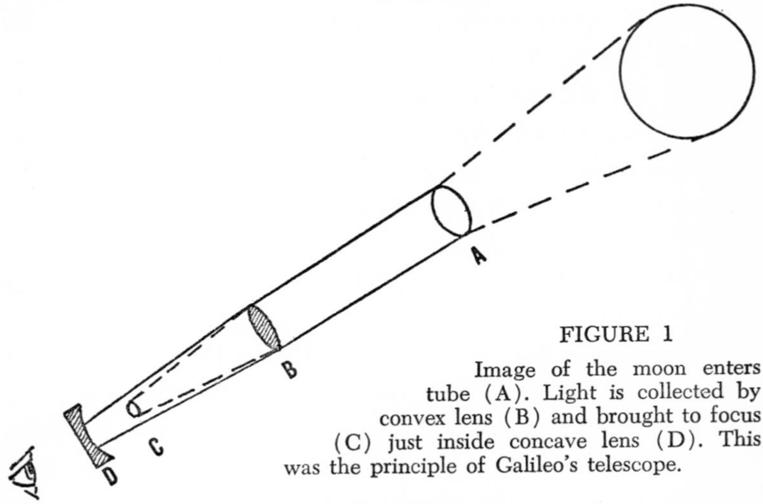

FIGURE 1

Image of the moon enters tube (A). Light is collected by convex lens (B) and brought to focus (C) just inside concave lens (D). This was the principle of Galileo's telescope.

Despite these difficulties, Galileo's discoveries of new worlds in outer space were as exciting to him as the discovery of a new land was to Christopher Columbus. He saw that the "man in the moon" was a pattern of mountains and valleys, although many men had insisted that the surface was perfectly smooth. Around the planet Jupiter he saw four brilliant tiny lights which he correctly believed to be Jupiter's moons. His eager eyes marveled at the spots on the sun, and soon he realized that this great fiery star turned on its own axis but did not revolve around the earth, as most

26

people commonly believed. Instead, the earth revolved around the sun!

This was not a new theory. It had been published many years before in a book by Nicolaus Copernicus, a Pole, and although Copernicus died in 1543, and had never looked through a telescope, he reasoned that the earth was merely one body among several which revolved around the sun.

Galileo's telescope proved to him that Copernicus was right, and he told the people of Padua what he had seen and what he believed. Some praised him, but others sneered.

"Who is this Galileo," they said, "to tell us that the Bible lies? Are we to throw away our Bibles and listen to him instead?"

The Bible says that the sun rises and sets, and that Joshua once commanded the sun to stand still, which it did. Now Galileo was telling the people that the sun did not really come up in the morning and go down at night, but only appeared to do so because the earth moved around it. He was a heretic, they said— a man who dared to question the Gospel and the teachings of the Church, who thought he knew more than Aristotle, more than all of the other learned scientists and astronomers.

In 1615, Galileo tried to use references from the Bible to support his arguments. The Bible, he said, was meant to teach men how to go to heaven—not how heaven goes. He was politely told by the high officers of the Church that he should stop this practice and limit his proofs to nonreligious reasoning.

The following year, in 1616, the Church made an official declaration that anyone who claimed that the sun was stationary and that the earth revolved around it was a heretic. Pope Paul V ordered Galileo not to "hold, teach, or defend" such a theory, and Galileo promised to obey, knowing that if he refused he would be jailed or tortured, or both.

Some of his feelings can be understood from an earlier letter he wrote to his friend Johann Kepler, the young assistant who inherited the notes left by Tycho Brahe.

"You are the first and almost the only person who, even after but a cursory investigation, has . . . given entire credit to my statements," Galileo wrote. "We will not trouble ourselves about the abuses of the multitude, for against Jupiter even giants, to say nothing of pigmies, fight in vain. Let Jupiter stand in the heavens and let the sycophants bark at him as they will."

In his letter he criticized the professors at the university where he taught mathematics. "I think, my Kepler," he wrote, "we will laugh at the extraordinary stupidity of the multitude. What do you say to the leading philosophers of the faculty here, to whom I have offered a thousand times . . . to show my studies, but who with the lazy obstinacy of a serpent who has eaten his fill have never consented to look at planets, nor moon, nor telescope? Verily, just as serpents close their ears, so do these men close their eyes to the light of the truth."

Although, for sixteen years Galileo kept his promise

to be silent, he continued his experiments and made notes in secret about his discoveries in the skies.

In 1632 he felt that he could keep still no longer, so he published a book in which he revealed the wonders he had seen and which supported the condemned theories of Copernicus. Galileo was acclaimed for the book throughout Europe—but in his own Italy the Church was angered and prohibited sales of the book there. On October 1, 1632, when he was commanded to appear before the Inquisition at Rome, Galileo protested that he was sixty-eight years old and in failing health. No matter, he was told. Be there!

He appeared before the Inquisition in Rome on February 13, 1633, but it was not until the following June that he had his hearing. Threatened with torture and imprisonment, Galileo was made to get down on his knees before a huge crowd, place his hand upon the Bible, and swear that the writings which he knew to be true were all lies.

He was held in custody from June 21 to June 24, and as part of his punishment he was ordered to recite once a week for three years the seven psalms of penitence. After living some months with a friend in Siena, Galileo went to his villa at Arcetri, near Florence, where he lived under guard for the next eight years. He continued to write until he finally lost his sight and his hearing. Pains in his legs and arms made it more and more difficult for him to sleep, and in 1642 he died at the age of seventy-eight, embittered against a world which had fought to keep the truth bottled up in his wonderful long glass eye.

The first improvement in the Galilean telescope was suggested by his friend, Johann Kepler. Kepler proposed using two convex lenses of different sizes instead of one convex and one concave lens, as Galileo had done. In this arrangement the image would be turned upside down to the eye of the observer, but Kepler decided that this would not make any important difference in looking at the moon and stars. The important thing was that it provided a much wider field of view in which no part of the light was wasted (Figure 2). Kepler himself apparently never made the improved telescope, but others did.

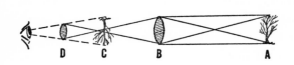

FIGURE 2

Kepler's suggested improvement on the Galilean telescope. Image of the tree enters tube (A). Light is collected by convex lens (B). Image is inverted (C), but second convex lens (D) gives much wider field of view than the concave lens.

Said by many to be the real founder of modern astronomy, Kepler established what are known as "Kepler's Laws," which were astronomical milestones. In simple language they are:

1. Each planet travels in an elliptical orbit with the sun

as a focal point. (Others had believed the orbits to be circles).

2. The radius vector of each planet covers equal areas in equal time. The radius vector is an imaginary line between sun and planet. This "law" means that the closer the planet is to the sun, the faster it travels.

3. The squares of the periods required by the planets to travel around the sun are equal to the cubes of their mean distances from the sun.

Thus Tycho Brahe, Galileo, and Kepler showed the way, and others profited by their discoveries to push forward to new horizons in science and astronomy through the telescope—but what unwieldy and mammoth inventions were to be built along the way!

CHAPTER THREE

THE GLASS EYE GROWS

Galileo's first telescope was no longer than your arm. Within a few years astronomers decided that bigger instruments would bring faraway objects closer and closer, and some telescopes finally reached a length of five or six feet.

A young Dutch mathematician named Christiaan Huygens, born at The Hague on April 14, 1629, wanted to look at the planet Saturn through a telescope of the kind in use about 1649, when he was only twenty years old. What he saw through this 5-foot tube only made him want to see more.

After many observations and months of study, Huygens decided that he must have a longer instrument, so in 1655, with his brother Constantijn, he ground and polished lenses for a telescope of his own making. It was twelve feet long—more than twice the size of any he had seen. With pounding heart and the excitement that comes with the exploration of the unknown, Huygens on March 25, 1655, turned his glass skyward toward Saturn the mysterious.

There, encircling the warm yellowish planet, was a wide, flat ring like some huge luminous hoop with

Saturn floating in its center! As Huygens gazed in surprise and wonder, he saw something else—a tiny light, like a small brilliant jewel.

For days Huygens studied the planet before he decided that the tiny glowing jewel was a moon (which today we call Titan). Other astronomers, looking through smaller telescopes, had detected light close to the planet and had said that Saturn must have two moons, but Huygens now knew that the light they had seen came from the great flat ring which their instruments were too weak to identify.

These were two startling discoveries. But what would a ring be doing around a planet? What was it made of? Could Huygens be wrong? He thought not. And yet . . . ? If he were right, he wanted credit for his find. He would continue his observations, but in the meantime he would protect his discovery. He published a mysterious code with which he believed he could prove his claim if it later became necessary. This was the code:

aaaaaaa ccccc d eeeee g h iiiiiii llll mm nnnnnnnnn oooo pp q rr s ttttt uuuuu.

Deciphered it read (in Latin), "Annulo cingitur, tenui, plano, nusquam cohaerente, ad eclipticam inclinato." The English translation is: "It (the planet) is girdled by a thin flat ring, nowhere touching, inclined to the ecliptic." The code itself was simple. In alphabetical order Huygens had assembled all the letters "a" from the Latin words, all the letters "c," and so on. If, then, he wrote the sentence intelligibly, all the letters would be used and none would be left over.

His claim was not opposed, and Huygens is credited with the discovery of Saturn's ring and her brightest moon (the planet has eight others, since identified).

Huygens also improved on the Keplerian eyepiece. The Huygens eyepiece, in use today, consisted of two small plano-convex lenses—flat on one side, bulging on the other (Figure 3). Here the field of vision is some four times greater than that of the Keplerian arrangement, and there is less chromatic aberration.

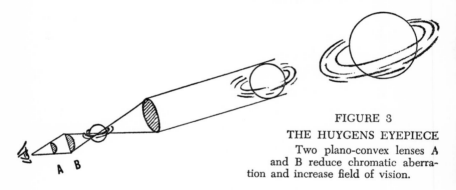

FIGURE 3
THE HUYGENS EYEPIECE
Two plano-convex lenses A and B reduce chromatic aberration and increase field of vision.

The Huygens telescope, in which light passed through three lenses of different sizes, tended to make each lens correct some of the chromatic aberration of the others; hence this type of eyepiece was later called *achromatic* (without color). This invention, however, was not Huygens' greatest accomplishment.

To measure time exactly—an important requirement in studying the stars—Huygens, in 1656, was the first to apply the pendulum to the regulation of clocks. He was the first to suggest that the twinkle of the stars was due to the effects of the earth's atmosphere, and that light traveled in waves, as water does. And he was the first to make a serious study of the Great Nebula of Orion, a cloud of cosmic dust and gas so huge that the sun, if engulfed by it, would be like a match in a forest fire.

News of Huygens' telescope soon reached Johann Hevelius, owner of a brewery in Danzig. Born January 28, 1611, Hevelius became so interested in astronomy that he built an observatory at his home. Convinced that long telescopes were more effective than short ones, Hevelius made an instrument 60 feet long, then followed it with another of 70 feet. Still not satisfied, he decided to build a telescope 150 feet in length!

He encountered a serious problem, however. He could not make a rigid tube of that size. One fashioned of iron would be far too heavy and too expensive. Paper was too fragile. After considerable study, Hevelius developed the novel idea of fastening two planks together at right angles to each other, like a trough. By joining several of these troughs end to end he had one very long V-shaped wooden framework in which he installed a lens (called "the objective") at one end, an eyepiece at the other. Spaced a few feet apart along the trough he fitted wooden blocks with holes in their centers, designed to keep stray light away from the eyepiece.

To raise this wooden giant skyward, Hevelius erected a pole about ninety feet high, with pulleys at its tip. With ropes through the pulleys, and with the necessary assistance of crowds of the townspeople who came to marvel at the sight, he managed to haul the objective end of his 150-foot trough toward the stars. Alas, it was not very stable. It trembled in the wind, the ropes would shrink in the damp air, and if there were any indications that a storm might approach, the telescope was not erected—or, if it was already up, it was taken down—an operation which required much time and labor.

With his "aerial telescope" and other telescopes, however, Hevelius and his wife, Elizabeth, mapped the surface of the moon, discovered four new comets, catalogued 1,564 stars, and made many observations of the terrific solar disturbances we call sunspots.

The craze for bigger telescopes was in full swing.

Christiaan Huygens, who had started it, was not to be left out. With his brother he built a telescope 170 feet long, another measuring 210 feet.

In France, a physicist named Adrien Auzout, believing there were animals on the moon, intended to make a telescope powerful enough to see them. Meager accounts of Auzout's experiments indicate that he made one instrument 300 feet long, which proved to be a pygmy compared to one which itself seemed long enough to reach the moon. It measured 600 feet, which is 45 feet higher than the Washington Monument! Obviously these incredible structures were too unwieldy for practical use, and Auzout never succeeded in getting a peek at his moon creatures.

Probably the most significant feat accomplished with an aerial telescope was recorded December 27, 1722, when an English astronomer and clergyman named James Bradley used an instrument about 212 feet long to measure the diameter of the planet Venus (about 7,700 miles).

Three years later, Bradley discovered that the human eye, looking at the light from a star, was not actually looking at the star itself. He also established another fact which settled an argument of long standing, by proving beyond any question that the earth travels around the sun. Both discoveries were made with a telescope set up in a cellar!

The cellar was in the home of his friend, Samuel Molyneux, in Surrey. The telescope, some 24 feet long and nearly 4 inches in diameter, was the handiwork of George Graham. To set it up, Bradley and Molyneux cut holes in the roof and all floors of the house, inserted the telescope, and secured it with iron braces fastened to two chimneys.

Their plan was to measure changes in the position of a single star by pinpointing it from the same place every night. By installing the telescope within the house the men knew it could not be disturbed by rain, wind, or other factors encountered in the open. Actually this method had been tried by another astronomer, Robert Hooke, in his own home, but without success.

Lying on a couch in the cellar, with his head directly under the eyepiece of the telescope, Bradley selected the star known as *Gamma Draconis* as his target, and began his observations on December 3, 1725. For several nights the star appeared in the same position, but on December 17, it seemed to have moved a little southward, and Bradley and Molyneux thought that the telescope might have been moved accidentally, or that Bradley had been mistaken in his observations. As nights passed, however, the star went farther south, and Bradley knew he was on the verge of a remarkable discovery. But what made the star move or seem to move?

Bradley allegedly found the answer to his puzzle when he was aboard a boat on the Thames River. He noticed that if the boat changed its course the flag that flew from its mast followed neither the direction of the boat nor of the wind. He asked a member of the crew about this phenomenon.

"Well, sir," the sailor told him, "the bloomin' flag can't help itself, it can't. If the boat sails crosswise, and the wind blows lengthwise, and if they both travels, say, ten knots, then the flag flies in the middle —on the diagonal, you might say."

Reflecting on this explanation, Bradley realized that the rotation of the earth, together with its movement around the sun, helps to change the direction of light from the stars. Perhaps you have stood under an umbrella in a rainstorm, with the rain falling straight down. Standing quietly, you would not be pelted by the drops, but if you were to move forward it would appear that the rain was changing its direction and veering directly toward you. The same thing happens to the starlight with respect to the moving earth, and is what we call the *aberration of light*. In addition, the starlight is bent, or refracted, by the earth's atmosphere, much as a stick seems to be bent when partly submerged in clear water.

Bradley's discovery of the aberration of light was one of the most important in the field of physical science. It was eventually of great value in establishing the theory of relativity, and was a vital factor in making stellar measurements.

Measurements made with telescopes were becoming more and more important to astronomers. In Middleton, England, a spider and a twenty-year-old youth named William Gascoigne pushed science forward another step in 1638, when Gascoigne invented the filar (threadlike) micrometer, or telescopic sight. Gascoigne, member of a group of amateur astronomers, used a Keplerian telescope. He found that if a thread were placed at the point where a magnified image was brought into focus, the thread would also be magnified.

This was a highly important discovery, since it provided an accurate method for measuring angles and diameters. By crossing two threads at right angles a center point could be easily fixed. Ordinary thread, however, was too thick for precise measurements, and Gascoigne evidently used the delicate strands of a spider's web in his instrument.

Although Gascoigne made many measurements of celestial bodies and kept records of his observations, most of these were lost, and only some of his letters to friends remained to testify to his work and discoveries. Gascoigne was killed July 2, 1644, at the

Battle of Marston Moor, near York. He was only twenty-five years old.

Some fifteen years later, in 1659, Christiaan Huygens wrote about an eyepiece micrometer which he had developed. Huygens' device was a metal wedge, placed in the focal plane of the telescope. This tapered piece of metal could be centered on a star or other object and adjusted until the metal barely covered it. By a scale, Huygens could then measure its diameter. His measurements were later found to be wrong, due mostly to the fact that his telescopes were far from perfect.

The micrometer was of great value to another English astronomer, Edmund Halley, who went to St. Helena, in February, 1677, to make a survey of stars in the little-known south polar skies. With his equipment, which included two micrometers, he was the first to catalogue the positions of 341 southern stars. Halley later became Astronomer Royal of England.

Halley's specialty was comets, and somewhere in outer space is one of the most spectacular of these fiery-tailed visitors, known to us as "Halley's Comet."

Halley, the son of an English soap boiler, was born November 8, 1656, in London. When he was fifteen he was rather tall and lanky, and a prize pupil at St. Paul's School in London, where he concentrated on Greek, Latin, Hebrew, mathematics and astronomy. At seventeen he entered Queens College, accompanied by a "a curious apparatus" of instruments, including a 24-foot telescope.

Halley had learned from a study of Tycho Brahe's observations that comets traveled around the sun, but no one knew exactly what course they took. By plotting the paths of twenty-four comets, and with the help of his telescope, Halley established definitely that their orbits were elliptical. (The word "comet" is derived from the Latin and Greek terms meaning "hair.")

In 1682, when the world was terrified by the appearance of the most awesome of the fiery streaks, the twenty-six-year-old Halley was delighted with the opportunity to get a close look at it, and after the comet whizzed off into space, Halley startled the astronomical world by declaring that it would be back again in seventy-six years—in 1758. Many scoffed, saying that Halley was safe in making his prediction because he would be dead by that time. Halley died January 14, 1742, but his prediction did come true, for the comet appeared on schedule and it has continued to return in seventy-six-year cycles—in 1834, and again in 1910. If it does not disintegrate or explode in outer space, it should next be visible in 1986 —so have your telescope ready for one of the greatest celestial fireworks displays of all time!

Telescope makers were striving to produce better instruments, but were hindered by chromatic and spherical aberration. Christiaan Huygens' achromatic eyepiece helped somewhat to correct the former, but it was not completely achromatic. Spherical aberration presented a different kind of lens problem.

Spherical aberration occurs in lenses with spherical

41

surfaces. The center of such a lens is thicker than the outer edges. The light passing through the outer edges is refracted (bent) at a sharper angle than that striking the thicker portion. Consequently some rays come into focus closer to the lens than others, so the viewer does not see the image clearly.

One solution for this problem was born in 1663, in the mind of a Scottish mathematician and astronomer named James Gregory, who conceived the idea of using two concave mirrors, one big, one small, instead of the customary lenses; a small lens was used for the eyepiece. He made a drawing of this *reflecting* telescope, showing that the light, or image, coming through the tube, would meet the large concave mirror near the eyepiece, and that this large mirror had an opening for the eyepiece itself. In front of the eyepiece, facing both it and the large mirror, was the small mirror. Gregory reasoned that the image would be reflected from the large to the small mirror, and again reflected through the eyepiece, and that since it did not have to pass through lenses, as in the *refracting* telescopes, there could be no spherical aberration (Figure 4).

The principle was sound, but lack of optical skill made it impossible for Gregory to build the telescope. Opticians had formed a union known as "the worshipful company of spectacle makers," and described their work as "the art and mistry of spectacle-making," but not one could solve the "mistry" of, or was artistic enough to manufacture, concave mirrors with the precise curvatures necessary to the successful construction of Gregory's instrument. Gregory went to several lens makers who tried for months—and failed—to meet his exacting specifications. In disgust, Gregory left England for Italy, where he continued his studies of mathematics and astronomy.

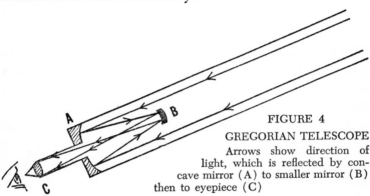

FIGURE 4

GREGORIAN TELESCOPE

Arrows show direction of light, which is reflected by concave mirror (A) to smaller mirror (B) then to eyepiece (C)

Unknowingly, James Gregory had launched a new era in the development of the telescope and the progress of astronomy. His drawing of the reflecting telescope came to the attention of one of the world's great scientists, Sir Isaac Newton—the same Newton who allegedly solved the puzzle of gravitation when he saw an apple fall. In 1668, when Newton was only twenty-five years old, he studied Gregory's drawing, decided he could improve upon it, and then built the first workable reflecting telescope. Newton was the first of those who literally peered through the looking glass to learn more about the wonderland of space— the mirror men.

CHAPTER FOUR

THE MIRROR MEN

Newton's improvement on James Gregory's idea was as unusual as it was simple. Instead of looking through one end of the telescope, Newton's was designed so that the viewer gazed into it through the side!

To make his mirror, Newton used a white metal instead of glass. Called "bell metal" because it was commonly used to manufacture school bells, it was made of three-fourths copper, one-fourth tin, was silvery in appearance and could be polished to a bright reflecting surface. Frequent polishing was needed because the high copper content caused the mirror to tarnish rather quickly.

Instead of the curved small mirror, which Gregory could not perfect, Newton used a flat one, two inches in diameter. He still used a large concave mirror, known as a "speculum," at one end of the instrument to pick up and reflect the image, but he made the mistake of giving the speculum a spherical instead of a paraboloidal curve. Technically this shaping is called "figuring."

A *paraboloid* is defined as "a solid or surface generated by the revolution of a parabola about its axis, or one some of whose plane sections are parabolas." A parabola is a curve formed by the intersection of a

cone with a plane parallel to a side of the cone. The
reflectors of most automobile headlights are paraboloidal. This type of curve virtually eliminates all
spherical aberration, and a mirror has no chromatic
aberration.

In Newton's first reflector, the small mirror was
fixed at a 45-degree angle, so that it picked up the
image from the curved mirror and reflected it through
the eyepiece to the observer (see Figure 5). The paraboloidal telescope mirror was yet to come.

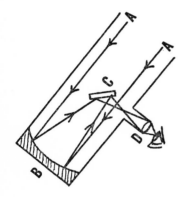

FIGURE 5

NEWTON'S REFLECTOR

Light (A) is reflected by concave
mirror (B) to small flat mirror (C)
to eyepiece (D).

Although Newton could see the satellites of Jupiter
with his instrument, this first reflecting telescope was
of little practical use for astronomy, and only Newton
and his close friends knew of its existence. Three
years later, however, in 1671, Newton made a second
reflector that was also of little astronomical value, but
it was a great step forward scientifically, and he was
asked to show it to the Royal Society of London for
Improving Practical Knowledge, the oldest scientific

society in Great Britain. The instrument was acclaimed and Newton was elected a Fellow of the Society, which today owns his second telescope.

Newton's studies of gravity won him immortality in the scientific world. He was deeply interested in Kepler's "laws," and Newton's observations eventually revealed the secret of planetary motion. Quite simply, he established that matter attracts matter with a force governed by the masses of the objects and the distances between them. This is the Law of Gravitation, and it explains why the earth and other planets are held to their orbits around the sun, by the latter's gravitational pull. Without this force, our earth would fly off into space like the weight hurled into the air by a hammer thrower.

Newton's findings showed that Kepler's "laws" were correct, but that they were merely the *results* of the Law of Gravitation.

Just as Newton, the Englishman, made changes in the telescope designed by the Scotsman, James Gregory, so did a Frenchman, Guillaume (William) Cassegrain, improve on both. Cassegrain, a noted sculptor whose hobby was astronomy, proposed the use of a small convex mirror instead of Newton's straight mirror. He also suggested that the large concave objective mirror be perforated in the center, as Gregory had shown it (see Figure 6). The small convex mirror, catching the reflection from the large concave mirror, would offset any spherical aberration in both. Also, this arrangement would require a comparatively short tube.

The idea was good (it is in use today), but apparently the British took the position that no Frenchman could possibly improve upon a telescope designed by the great Sir Isaac Newton. Newton himself was not bashful in criticizing Cassegrain's brain child.

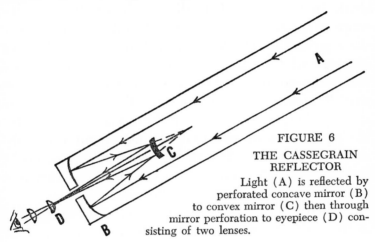

FIGURE 6

THE CASSEGRAIN
REFLECTOR

Light (A) is reflected by perforated concave mirror (B) to convex mirror (C) then through mirror perforation to eyepiece (D) consisting of two lenses.

"The advantages of this design are none," Newton said, "but the disadvantages are so great and unavoidable that I fear it will never be put in practice with good effect."

Cassegrain took this criticism to heart, and little more was heard about him or his telescope for a long time. The difficulties in making properly curved mirrors for reflecting telescopes were so great that no worth-while instruments of this kind were created until some fifty-three years after Newton's first model appeared.

The man generally credited with producing the

first practical reflecting telescope was John Hadley. Born in 1682, Hadley was filled with a curiosity which he satisfied by trying his hand at inventions. A contrivance in a waterworks near London Bridge "for raising and falling the water wheel" was his handiwork. In 1720 or 1721, Hadley made a reflecting telescope of the Newtonian design. The mirrors, or specula, were ground by Hadley and his brothers, George and Henry, and were far superior to those used in Newton's original instrument. The large concave mirror was 6 inches in diameter and the telescope was slightly longer than 62½ inches. Careful tests by Hadley convinced him that his instrument was fully as effective as the 123-foot refracting telescope made by Christiaan Huygens, which was nearly twenty-five times longer than Hadley's reflector.

Hadley later became world-famous as the inventor of the sextant, used today (at sea or in the air) to determine latitude by measuring the angle between the horizon and the sun or a certain star. His practical reflecting telescope, however, revived interest in this type of instrument, and he made no secret of his method of grinding metal-alloy mirrors with sand and emery, polishing them to a lustrous sheen with a curved glass disk covered with silk dipped in pitch.

To test the curvature of his mirrors, Hadley devised a system which was the forerunner of a better one developed more than a hundred years later by Jean Bernard Léon Foucault, a French physicist. Basically, Hadley's idea was to shine a light through a pinhole to the center of the mirror, then to look at the reflection through an eyepiece. If the image was not perfectly round, then he knew that his mirror, or some portion of it, was not properly curved.

Despite Hadley's success with mirrors, the reflecting telescope was not popular or in widespread use until several years after his first one was made. In 1732, word of Hadley's method reached a twenty-two-year-old Scot named James Short, who was in the University of Edinburgh studying for the ministry when he became deeply interested in astronomy and in the reflecting telescope.

Short made one of these instruments at the college, and it was so effective that he was besieged with requests to make others for sale. He won considerable fame in Great Britain for the excellence of his reflecting telescopes, though they were still far from perfect by later standards.

Reflecting telescopes also brought into focus the name of an eighteenth century genius who is credited with being the real father of modern astronomy. He was Friedrich Wilhelm Herschel, later more commonly known as Sir William Herschel. He was born November 15, 1738, in Hanover, Germany, where he was an outstanding student of music who mastered several instruments.

When he was only nineteen his father sent him to England to make his living. There Herschel taught music, organized and conducted a military band, and at twenty-eight became organist of the Octagon Chapel in Bath, the town where he later lived with his sister Caroline and his brother Alexander.

Herschel was primarily a musician, and it was not until he was about thirty-four that he began to devote his leisure to studies of mathematics and astronomy, in which he had been interested as a boy. "Leisure" meant perhaps a few minutes during the day, and two or three hours in the quiet of the night, when the town slept, for Herschel was not only a church organist, a music teacher, and a band leader—he was also Music Director for the city of Bath. This made him a kind of "booking agent," since it was his job to hire artists for concerts, to organize musical programs, and to make musical arrangements for anthems to be sung by the Chapel choir.

In 1773, Herschel decided to explore the heavens for himself. He bought lenses and first constructed a 4-foot Huygens refracting telescope, but this was too small to satisfy him, so he built another which measured 12 feet, followed by a third of 15 feet and a fourth measuring 30 feet.

"The great trouble occasioned by such long tubes which I found it almost impossible to manage," Herschel said, "induced me to turn my thoughts to reflectors."

He first rented a Gregorian reflector, two feet long. Unable to find larger instruments, he decided to build one of his own. With the help of a neighbor who was a mirror maker, Herschel learned how to grind and polish mirrors, then set about in earnest to make telescopes better than any he had seen.

Almost overnight, the Herschel home was transformed from a quiet haven for a music-loving family

50

into a veritable and noisy factory. Based on plans drawn by William, brother Alexander set up a lathe in one bedroom and produced patterns for the making of lenses and grinding tools. In the parlor, carpenters sawed and planed and hammered to make telescope tubes and mountings for them. William himself worked at the grinding, polishing and figuring of the mirrors, and so intent was he upon this work that he might have starved were it not for his sister Caroline.

Caroline, herself a fine musician and singer, wrote that in 1775 much of her time was spent in "attendance on my brother when polishing, since, by way of keeping him alive, I was constantly obliged to feed him by putting victuals by bits into his mouth." The reason for this was that Herschel, using emery to grind and polish his mirrors, insisted upon maintaining smooth, steady strokes which he would not interrupt even to take food, and sometimes he worked for sixteen hours at a stretch without taking his hands from the mirror.

For diversion, Caroline frequently read books aloud to her brother as he worked, and gradually she began to assist in some of the minor tasks. In her own words, she became "as useful a member of the workshop as a boy in the first year of his apprenticeship."

Herschel's intense interest in telescopes may be measured by his persistence. He set out to make a Gregorian reflector about 66 inches long. The first mirror was imperfect. The alignment was wrong, and he tried once to correct it, then again and again. Unwilling to admit defeat, Herschel made *two hundred*

separate attempts before he finally turned to the Newtonian design and produced an instrument which
satisfied him. And his satisfaction was great indeed
when, on March 4, 1774, using his own telescope, he
observed Saturn's rings and the Great Nebula of Orion
in all their celestial majesty.

This close look at these stellar attractions marked
the beginning of the end of the musical career in
which Herschel had also won considerable fame.
From the time he first gazed through his homemade
reflector, until he died, Herschel's efforts were directed
toward further exploration of the skies.

Promptly the Herschels moved to another house in
Bath—a house that had a yard large enough for William to install bigger telescopes! Eventually he did
make a 10-foot instrument and, with Caroline taking
notes, made extensive celestial observations for a
"comprehensive survey of the heavens." He was still
conducting occasional concerts in a theater near his
home, and on clear nights it was not an uncommon
sight to see him, resplendent in white ruffled jabot and
powdered wig, running homeward during intermis-
sion to take a fast look at the stars. His personal
affairs and his own health were secondary to astronomy and his telescopes, and on one occasion Herschel
is said to have made observations continuously for
three days and three nights, finally collapsing into a
deep sleep which lasted for more than twenty-four
hours.

In 1777, the Herschels moved again, this time closer
to the town center, to a house where William could

make and erect new telescopes which would be huge in comparison to all known reflectors. While experimenting with a 20-foot Newtonian he completed two smaller instruments. With one of these, measuring 7 feet, he made a study of "double stars," or stars whose light paths are so close together that they seem to be from a single source. Herschel compiled the very first catalogue of these double stars in 1779.

On March 13, 1781, Herschel made a discovery which was to change his professional future. Using the 7-foot reflector, he saw a new light in the heavens, and he trembled with excitement. This was no new star, no comet. It was bigger than the earth, almost two billion miles from the sun—it was a new planet! Furthermore, it was the first planet to be discovered with a telescope. Herschel named it Georgium Sidus. Today we call it Uranus.

Following this discovery, which won him international acclaim, Herschel in 1782 accepted an offer from King George III to give up his music entirely and to become England's Astronomer Royal.

His every thought and act was now directed toward the heavens. He tried to make a 30-foot reflector, but had great difficulty with the metal intended for the mirror. His first attempt failed when the mirror cracked while cooling. His second failed when the melting oven leaked and the molten metal spurted over the cellar floor. The workmen fled in terror. Herschel collapsed on a pile of bricks—safe, but so weary and shaken that he decided to stop work on the project.

In 1786, however, he designed and supervised the construction of a giant reflector with a sheet-iron tube 40 feet long and 5 feet in diameter! His sister Caroline later recalled that "The garden and workrooms were swarming with laborers and workmen, smiths and carpenters, going to and fro between the forge and the 40-foot machinery, and I ought not to forget that there is not one screw-bolt about the whole apparatus but what was fixed under the immediate eye of my brother. I have seen him lie stretched for many an hour in burning sun across the top beam whilst the iron work for the various motions was being fixed."

The mirror was the all-important part of the instrument. It was to be 48 inches in diameter—the biggest ever made, up to that time, and a tremendous undertaking.

Some twelve men helped to fashion the mirror, while others built a huge framework about five stories high to support the telescope tube. Visitors included not only the townspeople, but also the King himself and the Archbishop of Canterbury. Caroline, with obvious enjoyment, recalled one visit during which the King stepped into the iron tube as it lay on the ground. He beckoned to the Archbishop.

"Come, my lord Bishop," the King said, "I will show you the way to Heaven!"

When the tube was ready to be erected, the Herschels stood inside it and sang a song. Some fifty years later, on New Year's Eve in 1839, when the tube had again been lowered to the ground, Herschel's son

John and his family once again stood in it and sang a ballad written by John. The tube was left on the ground for several years and was partially destroyed by a tree which was blown down upon it in a storm.

John Herschel, Sir William's son, became famous not only as an astronomer in his own right, but also as a chemist. It was he who, in 1839, invented the use of sensitized paper in photography, and who first used the terms "negative" and "positive" for photographic negatives and prints.

Caroline also became an astronomer of some note. She ground and polished lenses, worked through the long nights making observations and aiding her brother. She is credited with the discovery of at least eight comets and of other astronomical "firsts."

Herschel's telescopes were of such excellence that they were greatly in demand, and to help support himself and Caroline he made and sold several, ranging in price from $1,000 to $15,000. His tremendous 40-foot telescope did not come up to his expectations, although he did discover new satellites of Saturn with it, and confirmed observations he had made with smaller instruments. He catalogued some 800 double stars and increased the number of observed nebulae (gas clouds or distant star clusters) from 100 to about 2,500. A ticking tribute to his skill and precision is an immense "great-great-grandfather's" clock, some fifteen feet tall and nearly a yard wide, which, as this is written, is in the American Museum-Hayden Planetarium, New York City. This massive timepiece was built by Herschel in 1806, adjusted in 1918, and was readjusted by the Longines Wittnauer Watch Company in 1956. It still keeps excellent time.

Herschel died August 25, 1822, at the age of eighty-four, and Caroline went to live in Hanover, Germany, where she died January 9, 1848. She was ninety-eight years old. Asked one day about the sleepless hours she devoted to her brother's work she said, "I did nothing for him except what a well-trained puppy dog would have done."

While the attention of the scientific world was centered largely upon the usefulness and advantages of reflecting telescopes, there were some who disagreed with Newton's statement that the refractor could not be improved. Achromatic and spherical aberration were still important obstacles which might be removed.

In Essex, England, a scientist named Chester Moor Hall used the human eye as the basis for detailed studies of lenses. There are three parts of the eye which refract light—the aqueous humor, the lens, and the vitreous humor—and in looking at the world around us, we are not troubled by chromatic aberration. Hall believed that it might be possible to combine glass lenses to achieve the same desirable result.

After long experimenting, Hall made a telescope objective using one piece of "crown" glass and one piece of "flint" glass. Crown glass was a common type of hard glass used for the making of spectacles. Flint glass had a high content of lead oxide, which gave it a brilliance that is today highly prized in expensive

crystal. In combination, lenses of both glasses produced an image which was almost completely achromatic—virtually free of color aberration.

In 1733, Hall took into his confidence a London
optician named George Bass, asking Bass to make
several of the new telescope objectives. If Hall
thought his discovery would startle the astronomical
world, he was sadly mistaken. Although Bass let other
opticians in on the secret, they had difficulty in finding
glass of the quality required, and Hall's solution of the
color aberration problem gained little notice until a
quarter of a century later, when it became the center
of a bitter court battle.

The battle began over an application for a patent
for achromatic lenses, submitted by John Dollond and
his son, Peter. John Dollond was an English silk
weaver, son of a Huguenot refugee. When he was
forty-six years old he abandoned the weaving trade
to go into business with his son, a manufacturer of
optical instruments.

Unlike Hall, who had tried to restrict his own
secret, Dollond wrote a long report to the Royal
Society that he had succeeded in perfecting his invention only after months of trial and error. He was
awarded a medal and acclaimed as the inventor of the
achromatic lens.

Chester Moor Hall brought suit in court to prove
that he, not Dollond, had invented the color-free lens
many years earlier. He pointed out that during all the
intervening years it would have been easy for Dollond to learn the secret from the opticians to whom it

had been revealed by Bass. The court, however, awarded the patent to the Dollonds, who immediately started to produce the revolutionary lenses in a London shop with the quaint name of "The Sign of the Golden Spectacles and Sea Quadrant."

The Dollond lens combination was similar to that in present use. It consisted of a convex lens of crown glass fitted snugly against a concave lens of flint glass (see Figure 7). The convex lens focused colors at one point, the concave lens at another. Together, they brought colors into focus at the same point.

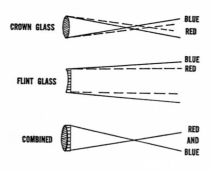

FIGURE 7

THE DOLLOND
ACHROMATIC LENS

Convex crown glass combined with concave flint glass brought colors to focus at single point.

Later, Peter Dollond made a three-piece achromatic lens having a double concave lens between two convex lenses, sandwich-style.

The rivalry between refractor and reflector seesawed more than ever. In 1770, a Swiss cabinetmaker and chemist named Pierre Louis Guinand dismantled a reflecting telescope borrowed from a friend, and carefully examined every part. After several attempts he succeeded in casting a metal mirror and making a telescope of his own. He also undertook a study of optical glass and discovered a way to make perfect disks for lenses.

This discovery resulted from Guinand's use of fire clay for stirring his molten glass. Like other lens makers, he had used a wooden stick as a stirrer, but the glass generally cooled with bubbles and streaks, making much of it useless for optical purposes. When Guinand used a fire-clay stirrer, however, the bubbles came to the surface and the glass cooled evenly, without flaws, making it suitable for perfect lenses.

A contemporary who once worked with Guinand, and who later was acknowledged to be a world authority on optics, was Joseph von Fraunhofer. The son of a master glazier, Fraunhofer was born March 6, 1787, in Bavaria. When he was twelve years old his parents had died and he was sent to Munich as an apprentice to a miserly mirror maker who refused to let the boy attend school.

At nineteen, Fraunhofer was an expert glass cutter and engraver, and was offered a job working with Guinand in the Munich Institute. The two did not like each other and in 1814 Guinand returned to his home in Switzerland.

From exhaustive studies of defects in optical glass, Fraunhofer learned how to produce the finest telescope lenses of his time. He also became famous for his studies of the spectrum, as we shall later see.

Fraunhofer died of tuberculosis when he was only thirty-nine years old, and was buried at Munich.

Because of his progressive work, the refracting telescope was again on the upswing, and many astronomers now felt that the reflector was becoming obsolete. One who disagreed was William Parsons, the Earl of Rosse, an Irish engineer and astronomer. The entire village of Parsonstown, Ireland, was part of his earldom, and it was there that he set up a factory and trained men to make parts for reflecting telescopes.

One of Parsons' inventions was a machine for grinding and polishing mirrors—a tedious job that had always been done by hand. His device was the predecessor of those in use today.

After producing mirrors ranging in diameter from 6 to 36 inches, Parsons set out to make what was then the world's largest reflecting telescope—an instrument of Newtonian design with a metal mirror measuring 6 feet in diameter and weighing some four tons.

The metal, after heating for an entire day, was poured at night and outdoors in the castle grounds. The night was clear and the moon bright, but the men sweating in front of the melting furnace could see no moon or stars. Yellow flames belched from the furnace doors. The molten metal, like liquid gold, flowed into three huge crucibles which were hauled through the air on a framework to the casting pit for the mirror. The fiery mass was poured into the mold, shooting glowing drops skyward like a flaming fountain, and shadows of men and trees danced grotesquely on the castle walls.

The mirror cooled for some four months. When grinding began, the mirror broke. Another was made, but was imperfect. Parsons refused to be discouraged.

One after another, three more mirrors were cast before he obtained satisfactory results.

It took Parsons and his workmen about two years to construct a mounting (framework) strong enough to hold this gigantic reflector. The mounting, resembling some strange kind of fortified stronghold, consisted of two walls of stone and mortar, each seventy-two feet long and fifty-six feet high. They stood twenty-four feet apart to allow enough room for the massive skeleton of iron and wood which would hold the telescope and permit its movement.

The mounting was finished in 1844. In 1845, the three-year job of grinding and polishing the huge mirror was completed, and the challenging task of placing the tube and mirror in place was begun. The four-ton mirror must be installed in a tube 56 feet long and 8 feet in diameter—much like the boiler of a twentieth century locomotive, except that the tube was made of wooden planks ringed by iron hoops. Parsons' engineering skill was of invaluable aid, and with a highly complicated system of weighted levers, ball-and-socket joints and triangles, he succeeded in placing his instrument in position.

People came for miles to see the telescope, which was known as "The Leviathan of Parsonstown." Although it aroused new interest in the reflector, Parsons' instrument did not bring about any world-shaking discoveries in the heavens.

One of the greatest developments in the reflecting telescope originated in 1835, when a thirty-two-year-old German chemist named Justus von Liebig discovered a method of coating a glass with silver. Apparently his invention attracted little attention among astronomers, for it was twenty-two years before the "silvering" process was applied to telescope mirrors. In 1857, the Frenchman, Jean Bernard Léon Foucault, discovered the process for himself.

Foucault, son of a Paris publisher, was born September 18, 1819. In his comparatively short life of forty-nine years he invented the gyroscope, used a pendulum to demonstrate conclusively the rotation of the earth, measured the velocity of light, and devised a method of making telescope mirrors of proper paraboloid figure and of testing them for perfect curvature.

The coating of glass with silver simplified many of the problems of the reflecting telescope. Both the "reflectorites" and the "refractorites" were making superior claims for their respective types of instruments, and both kinds were in wide use. Telescope-making had begun in Europe, and telescopes of European manufacture were in operation in America. Even as late as 1847, no European astronomer gave the slightest thought to the possibility that the United States might invade the field of telescope-making. It was not long, however, before all Europe knew that such an invasion was under way.

It began with a 15-inch refractor made in Munich, Germany, for use in the Harvard Observatory, and with a boy turned artist and engraver—a Yankee farm boy named Alvan Clark.

CHAPTER FIVE

YANKEE GENIUS

The one hundred-acre farm in Ashfield, Massachusetts, where Alvan Clark was born March 8, 1804, was said by some to be "one of the roughest and rockiest in that rough and rocky town."

Two clear brooks murmured and swirled through the farm, and young Alvan knew all the pools and eddies where the trout lurked warily in the shade. He had little time for fishing, however, because after school he worked in a sawmill and a gristmill built beside the streams. He also liked to draw pictures more than he liked to fish, and by the time he was twenty-one years old he was quite accomplished in drawing and painting portraits.

One day some brushes he had ordered from Boston came wrapped in a piece of newspaper, and as Clark unfolded the paper a line in bold type caught his eye—ENGRAVERS WANTED. He read the advertisement, packed a bag and headed for Boston, where he landed a job as an engraver of designs for cloth prints. Salary: eight dollars per week.

Soon after his twenty-second birthday he married Maria Pease, of Enfield, Connecticut. For the next twenty years, while working as an engraver, he did not neglect his art, and eventually he opened a studio and devoted his full time to portrait painting.

It was by chance rather than design that Clark became interested in telescopes. In 1844, his eldest son, George Bassett Clark, was an engineering student at Phillips Andover Academy, where one of his subjects was astronomy. The boy, however, became more interested in how telescopes were made than in what they revealed in the skies.

One day the school's dinner bell was broken accidentally. George Clark, recalling that Isaac Newton had made his telescope mirrors with "bell metal," gathered up the pieces and at the first opportunity melted them in the kitchen of the Clark home in Cambridgeport, Massachusetts, casting the molten metal into a 5-inch disk. After reading whatever was available about telescope mirrors, the Clark boy began to grind the disk to the proper curvature, only to discover, as had others before him, that the grinding was hard work and that it was not easy to figure the mirror accurately. Finally he went to his father for advice and help.

Alvan Clark left his painting to help his son complete the mirror. First, though, he had to learn something about telescopes and optics. Later he wrote, "I was at some pains to acquaint myself with what had been done and how done in this curious art, that my son could have the benefit of my maturer judgment in giving effect to his experiments."

Together, father and son ground and polished the disk—the first product of what was to be one of the most important firms of American telescope makers, Alvan Clark and Sons (another son, Alvan G. Clark, later participated).

The mirror was barely completed before it began to tarnish. Alvan Clark said that this was a barrier they would undoubtedly meet in making any metal specula, so he suggested that they forget about making reflector telescopes and make refractors instead. This would involve the making of achromatic lenses, and such lenses should be of the quality of those produced by Joseph von Fraunhofer—or even better, if possible. No one in America was an expert in this European art, but Alvan Clark accepted the challenge and set out to meet it.

First he searched Boston for glass disks to be ground and polished. He bought cheap ones to be used for experiments, and spent weeks fashioning them into lenses, but the results were discouraging because he failed to produce the perfect curvature needed for first-quality glasses. In the midst of these experiments, the Harvard Observatory at Cambridge purchased a 15-inch refractor for $12,000 from a firm of telescope makers in Munich. This instrument was installed in 1847, when the Observatory itself was only eight years old.

Alvan Clark was anxious to see the new telescope and received permission not only to inspect it, but also to look through it. In the exciting moments that he stood in the cavernous observatory room, his sharp eyes intent upon the imported object glass, he realized that he had learned enough about lenses to know that the 15-inch European-made refractor was defective. Its imperfections were not great, but they were there and Clark could detect them—a discovery which convinced him that he could make objectives of better quality if he kept trying.

In the weeks that followed he reworked some of his imperfect disks and ground and polished new ones. Though each completed task added to his store of knowledge and his skill, he was not satisfied with the quality of his lenses and decided that the American glass he used was inferior to that obtainable abroad. He therefore ordered glass disks from Europe, which he ground and polished into objectives for a 5-inch refractor.

For seven years, Clark made telescopes with perfect disks ranging from five to eight inches in diameter. From his own observations he was satisfied that his instruments were superior to those of foreign manufacture, but as a business telescope-making in America brought no financial returns. Astronomers and institutions needing telescopes continued to buy them abroad, and if it were not for an English clergyman, Alvan Clark might have faded into obscurity like a dying star.

The clergyman was the Reverend W. R. Dawes of London, who was also an astronomer of note. In Clark's gleanings of astronomical activity he knew that the Reverend Dawes was especially interested in double stars, and Clark wrote Dawes a letter describing double stars which Clark had discovered with his telescopes. This began an exchange of correspondence, the gist of which was:

Dawes: Mr. Clark, what kind of telescopes are you using?

Clark: Clark telescopes. I make my own.

Dawes: Do I understand, sir, that you manufacture the entire instrument, lenses and all?

Clark: Correct.

Dawes: Your findings interest me greatly. I might be interested in buying one of your telescopes, but of course I would expect first to have it put to the test.

Clark: I'm agreeable. What kind of test do you want?

Dawes: As you probably know, Dr. Friedrich Georg Wilhelm Struve, director of the Russian observatory at Pulkowa, has listed several double stars which small telescopes (such as yours) could hardly resolve. The list is enclosed. Can your instruments detect and describe these double stars?

Clark: I have located every one. Here is my list and my complete description.

Dawes: I'm convinced! Send me one of your instruments right away.

Dawes soon asked for four additional telescopes, which Clark supplied. So gratifying were the results obtained with these instruments in England that in 1859 the minister insisted that Clark come to London to discuss his work.

Clark accepted the invitation and spent six weeks in

England, meeting the foremost astronomers of the Empire. His personality apparently made an impression as favorable as that made by his workmanship, for he received numerous orders for telescopes, not only from England but from other European nations as well.

The long hours of grinding and polishing, the years of study and of aiming at perfection, had paid off, for Alvan Clark and Sons was a thriving firm, destined to produce some of the world's greatest telescopes. The United States had established a firm foothold in the telescope-making business, and now other Americans began to emerge as experts in this unique field and in astronomical work.

John Alfred Brashear, for example, conquered obstacles which would have defeated many another dedicated man, to become one of the all-time great makers of telescopes. Brashear, son of a French Huguenot family originally named Brasseuir, was born November 24, 1840, in Brownsville, Pennsylvania, and was only nine years old when he had his first look at the sky. A McKeesport showman named Squire Wampler set up a telescope in Brownsville, where the boy's grandfather, an amateur astronomer, paid Wampler to let young John gaze through the instrument. Saucer-wide were the youthful eyes that saw Saturn's rings and the mountains of the moon, sights that made an indelible impression on the lad's mind.

Brashear's interest in astronomy never waned, and

he studied the heavens with his unaided eye for years, but as a teen-ager it became necessary for him to get a job. Actually he had several, varying from a printer's devil to grocery clerk to patternmaker—even to building coffins for an undertaker—and finally to mechanic (later foreman) in a Pittsburgh steel mill in 1861.

Still interested in the stars, John Brashear went to an optician to order an object glass with which he could assemble his own telescope, but the dealer took one look at this millworker in overalls and refused to make the glass. How would a mill hand know what to do with a telescope?

When Brashear told his wife, Phoebe, about this episode, she showed the kind of spirit which more than once was to keep him from utter discouragement. She reminded her husband that together they had built their home with their own hands. "If we can build a house," she told him, "we certainly ought to be able to make a telescope!"

In a coal shed in his yard Brashear set up a workshop, then ordered pieces of crown and flint glass through the New York office of a British optical firm. Though he worked at the mill from six in the morning until six (or later) every night, he and Phoebe Brashear (he called her "Ma") also worked until midnight at grinding and polishing his glasses.

When they were finally completed in 1875, he installed them in a wooden tube which he then stuck out of a window, aimed at the moon. Trembling with excitement and happiness, Brashear saw the familiar

69

mountains and valleys—and there was Saturn—beautiful, mysterious, ringed Saturn, just as he had seen it thirty-five years before.

"Ma" Brashear looked, too, and knew that all their work had been worth-while. Together they summoned their friends and neighbors, eager to have them see the wonders of the universe. John wrote later that one man wanted to look at "Juniper" and "Satan." Another seemed surprised because, he said, he had seen the very same stars when he lived in Germany.

Brashear took his lens to Dr. Samuel Pierpont Langley, then director of Allegheny Observatory in Pittsburgh, himself a famous astronomer. Langley congratulated him upon his capable work, but suggested that he make reflectors instead of refractors, and lent him a how-to-do-it book by Dr. Henry Draper.

Although Brashear was now a foreman at the mill, his hours had not changed and he could work at home only late at night. It took weeks of hard, tedious labor to grind, polish and figure a 12-inch objective, which Brashear then planned to coat with silver. For this the disk had to be heated. It was immersed in cold water, which was then warmed slowly. Finally the silver solution was emptied into the tank, and John and "Ma" Brashear watched the shiny metal cling to the glass.

It was a happy moment—but only a moment. Suddenly there was a sharp *crack!* The glass had broken.

70

So also, it seemed, had John Brashear's heart. In a split second, all the long nights of effort, the weary months of grinding and polishing had become merely time out of his life.

All that tragic night he lay awake, staring into the darkness of his bedroom, wondering why the glass had broken, wondering why he had thought he could succeed in the first place, wondering why—why, why, why?

At daybreak he rose, dressed, and went to the mill as usual, but things were not the same. He worked listlessly, weighted down by the burden of failure. As he trudged homeward that night he wondered if he would ever again attempt to make another mirror. The answer, prepared by Mrs. Brashear, was waiting for him at home.

"Ma" had cleaned his workshop, built a fire in the boiler of his little steam engine, and put out his working clothes. And there on one of the benches, like a rough diamond, was another glass disk ready for him to work on.

"Have your supper," Ma said, "and then we'll get to work." She patted the disk. "You'll see—this will be the best of them all."

She was right. Before coating the polished disk, John Brashear read everything he could find about the silvering process. Then he experimented by coating several fragments of plain glass, and as he worked he began to make little modifications and changes in the process. The result was that he developed a method of his own for the silvering process—an improved and simplified method which was soon adopted by mirror makers everywhere.

John Brashear finished his 12-inch reflector, which was the ancestor of many greater instruments. He became very friendly with Dr. Langley. "Of an afternoon," Brashear wrote later, "he would come over to my shop to watch the baseball games, as the park was in sight and a telescopic view of the game very satisfactory!"

In trying to work at the mill and also on his telescopes, Brashear suffered a nervous breakdown which made it necessary for him to choose one field or the other. He loved the stars, but he was in debt and not sure that he could make a living as a telescope manufacturer. Dr. Langley had an important part in helping Brashear make his decision.

Langley brought him to a wealthy Pittsburgh industrialist named William Thaw, who was interested in science and in Brashear's accomplishments. Thaw volunteered to furnish the money to establish him in the telescope-making business, and Brashear gave up his job at the mill. The business prospered and Brashear soon employed a young glassmaker, James B. McDowell, who gradually supervised the work of the firm as Brashear became more active in civic, educational, and cultural projects in which he was frequently honored publicly. To the people of Pittsburgh his long whiskers and bright eyes were familiar sights, and he became known affectionately as "Uncle John." He was the greatest lens maker of his time, and from the Brashear shops came many of the finest reflector and refractor telescopes in the United States.

When McDowell grew old he persuaded a young instrument maker named J. W. Fecker to come to Pittsburgh from Cleveland to join the firm. Fecker was the son of an intimate friend of Brashear, Gottlieb L. Fecker, noted for the excellence of his precision work in the manufacture of astronomical instruments. J. W. Fecker eventually succeeded Brashear and Mc-Dowell. Today the firm of J. W. Fecker, Inc., is a subsidiary of the American Optical Company, and continues to maintain the reputation for quality established more than seventy-five years ago by John Alfred Brashear.

Brashear died in 1920 and was cremated. His ashes, with those of his wife, lie at the base of a 30-inch reflector which he made and which was originally erected as a memorial to James Edward Keeler at the Allegheny Observatory, University of Pittsburgh. Brashear's epitaph was chosen from an anonymous poem which he loved, entitled *The Astronomer*. The epitaph reads: "We have loved the stars too fondly to be fearful of the night."

Allegheny Observatory, now one of the finest in the world, came into being on the tail of Donati's comet, named for its discoverer, the Italian astronomer Giovanni Battista Donati. When this space visitor brightened the skies in 1858 it roused considerable new interest in astronomy, and a group of Pittsburgh businessmen formed the "Allegheny Telescope Association" to buy a large telescope, "the magnifying power of which will bring the heavenly bodies near enough to be viewed with greater interest and satisfaction."

The Association bought a 13-inch refractor made by Fitz of New York, and in January, 1861, they housed it in a new domed observatory in what was then the city of Allegheny (later a part of Pittsburgh). For two years the telescope was used only occasionally, and during that time the observatory was unable to pay a salary which would attract a qualified director. In 1863, however, they hired an eccentric astronomer named Professor Philotus Dean.

Eccentric was the word for Philotus. He offered to work without pay if the Association would give him a rent-free home, which was done. When it was announced that he had taken up his duties at the observatory, a group of amateur astronomers arrived one night to look through the telescope and to talk with the professor about the stars. As they approached the door it was opened by Philotus—but instead of extending the hand of welcome, he pointed a shotgun at his visitors!

"What do you want?" he asked.

"We want to look at the stars," someone said.

"Not through my telescope!" Philotus snapped. He pointed the gun upward for an instant. "There they are. Go look at 'em!"

The stargazers gazed at each other. "But that's what the telescope is for," one said.

Professor Dean straightened up. "Sir," he said, "this telescope is not to be used, but preserved, and preserve it I shall!"

His preservation made little difference, for there was a great waning of interest in the telescope, and in 1867 the Association presented both instrument and building to the Western University of Pennsylvania —now the University of Pittsburgh. It was a notable year for one reason. A great physicist came to Pittsburgh as professor of astronomy and director of Allegheny Observatory. He was Samuel Pierpont Langley, then only 33 years old.

Born August 22, 1834, in Roxbury, Massachusetts, Langley graduated from Boston High School in 1851. Although he never went to college, in 1857 he went west to Chicago and St. Louis and worked as a civil engineer and architect for seven years. In 1864 he toured Europe for a year with his brother to broaden his education. When they returned to Boston in 1865, Langley accepted a post at Harvard Observatory, but a year later he became a teacher of mathematics at the U.S. Naval Academy at Annapolis, Maryland, where he stayed until he became director of Allegheny Observatory.

Langley's special astronomical interest was the sun. An accomplished draftsman, he made amazingly detailed drawings of sunspots, most famous of which was probably his drawing of the great sunspot of December, 1873. He proved that life on earth could not exist without dark (infrared) radiations from the sun, and he measured the heat of these and other solar radiations with an instrument of his own invention, called a bolometer.

With the aid of his friend, William Thaw, Langley

added to the observatory's equipment. One new instrument was a small telescope for observing stars as they crossed the meridian (an imaginary line of longitude curving from pole to pole) at the zenith (directly overhead). The exact position of any star could be calculated from a long series of previous observations, and at the moment a given star crossed the meridian it was possible to tell the exact time.

Langley arranged for telegraph lines to be installed from the observatory to Pittsburgh's city hall and to local railroads. Over these lines, for a fee, he flashed time signals by which clocks could be kept accurate. The payments for this service were used to finance astronomical research. Some four years later the U.S. Naval Observatory in Washington began to send time signals throughout the country, using "the Allegheny System."

On the night of July 8, 1872, after Langley left the observatory, someone stole the object glass of its 13-inch refractor. Promptly Langley had a brief letter published in *The American Journal of Science and Art,* telling of the theft and asking for the return of the lens. He promised no reward or remittance of punishment.

Some hinted that the lens had been stolen by Professor Philotus Dean, or at his instigation, but investigation failed to implicate him in any way.

Soon Langley received a letter from a stranger who wanted to talk with him about the stolen lens. They met in a lonely wooded spot, where the thief asked Langley for money for the return of the glass. Langley refused, saying that all thieves should be punished. Shortly after this meeting the lens was returned, but it was so badly scratched that it had to be refigured by Alvan Clark and Sons.

Samuel Langley remained at Allegheny for twenty years, leaving there to accept an appointment as director of the Smithsonian Institution in Washington, highest scientific office in the nation. There he won more fame when he built a steam-driven airplane model which (without a pilot) flew 4,200 feet, giving Langley the distinction of being the first man to make a powered heavier-than-air machine that would fly.

Other American astronomical observatories were either planned or in existence. Probably the first such observatory in America was that built by the University of North Carolina at Chapel Hill, North Carolina, completed in 1832. It had a short life, ending in a fire some six years later.

Others were begun at Williams College, Williamstown, Massachusetts, in 1836, at Harvard College (Dana House, 1839), and other institutions. Yale acquired a telescope in 1830, but had no observatory for some time.

The U.S. Naval Observatory in Washington, D. C., was an outgrowth of a Navy Department unit called "Depot of Charts and Instruments," set up in Washington in 1830 to provide safe navigation for American naval vessels. Today the Naval Observatory is one of the few institutions in the world—and the only one in the United States—where fundamental positions of sun, moon, planets and stars are continually determined, not only for navigation purposes, but also to provide accurate time.

Time is determined with telescopes known as photographic zenith tubes (PZT) fixed in a vertical position. One of these is in Washington; one in Richmond, Florida. For reflecting purposes a pool of liquid mercury is used instead of a mirror. On every clear night photographs are taken of stars as they pass the meridian near the zenith. Times of exposures are accurately recorded by a clock. The position of the star is known exactly, as the result of previous observations. By measuring the star photographs, the astronomer can determine what the clock read when the star was on the meridian. The difference between what the clock read and what it *should* have read tells how fast or slow the clock is—usually a few thousandths of a second. It is adjusted accordingly.

For years the Naval Observatory broadcast time signals to the country every hour. Today the time signals are broadcast from the National Bureau of Standards in Washington and the Naval Radio Station at Annapolis, Maryland, but the signals are monitored by the observatory and are still known as "Naval Observatory time signals."

The Naval Observatory has a station in Flagstaff, Arizona, where its largest telescope—a 40-inch reflector—is maintained. Biggest instrument in the Washington observatory is a 26-inch refractor, for which the object glass was made by Alvan Clark.

The Naval Observatory is open Monday through Friday, and guided tours are conducted every afternoon. On three nights each week (when the weather is clear) groups are permitted to look through the 26-inch telescope. The groups are limited to 120 persons each night, and the show is as successful as a smash hit on Broadway, with a six-month waiting list for tickets (free).

Other major American observatories are discussed in later chapters.

Granddaddies of the world's great observatories are the National Observatory in Paris, France, founded in 1667, and the Royal Observatory now at East Sussex, England, built in 1675 (originally at Greenwich). "Greenwich" has become a synonym for the zero meridian—the place where the time zones of the world begin. It was established to aid British navigators, and today all ships and planes reckon their longitudinal positions from its meridian.

The many observatories throughout the world would be of little practical use were it not for the frameworks, or mountings, which hold and move the telescopes. No one knows how Galileo kept his telescope steady when he observed the skies. Some say he rested it on a window sill. Others think he improvised a tripod or other mounting. All agree, however, that he had to do something to keep the instrument motionless, for the tiniest movement would be so greatly magnified that the careful observation of any celestial body would be impossible. Look at any star through a pair of binoculars held in your hands, and you will see one reason why telescope mountings are so important.

An American firm which became (and is) famous for its precision-built telescope mountings was founded by two New England Yankees, Worcester Reed Warner and Ambrose Swasey. Warner's interest in astronomy dated from his childhood, when his mother, an amateur astronomer, helped him to make a telescope from junked machine parts.

Still in his teens, Warner went to Exeter, New Hampshire, to become a machine-shop apprentice. There he met Swasey, and the two became good friends. In 1870, when they had learned their trade as machinists, they both landed jobs with the Pratt and Whitney Company in Hartford, Connecticut, and decided to pool their savings to build a fund for their futures.

It took them ten years to save enough money to establish a business of their own, and in 1880 they opened a machine shop in Chicago. Business was poor, so they packed up and moved to Cleveland, Ohio, where they enlisted the help of other machinists with whom they had worked at Pratt and Whitney. This time their venture succeeded, and although the new firm received orders for lathes and other machines, Worcester Warner proposed that they make telescopes and telescope mountings. Their first was a 9½-inch instrument, made for Beloit (Wisconsin) College. The mounting for the 26-inch refractor at the Naval Observatory was also their handiwork.

Today the names of these master builders are perpetuated in the Warner and Swasey Observatory in Cleveland, Ohio, and the firm they founded has be-

Tycho Brahe

Yerkes Observatory Photo

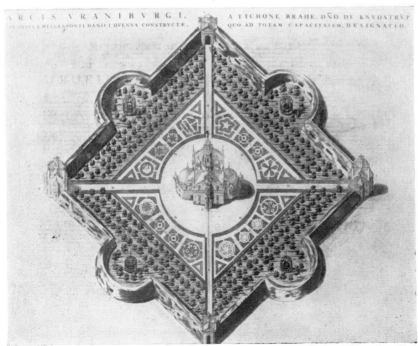

Yerkes Observatory Photo

Tycho Brahe's Observatory "Uraniborg," about 1584

Johann Kepler

Yerkes Observatory Photo

Yerkes Observatory Photo

Galileo Galilei

Galileo's Telescopes

Yerkes Observatory Photo

Christiaan Huygens

James Bradley who discovered
the aberration of light

Ancient quadrant used by
Hevelius

Sir Isaac Newton

Sir William Herschel

Herschel's 40-foot telescope and mounting

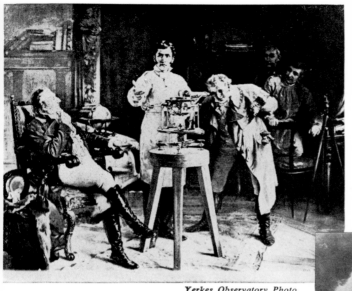

Joseph Von Fraunhofer (standing upright) demonstrates the spectroscope

Yerkes Observatory Photo

John A. Brashear, "The Man Who Loved the Stars"

→

Yerkes Observatory Photo

Lord Rosse's reflecting telescope

Yerkes Observatory Photo

The 26-inch refracting telescope in use at the U. S. Naval Observatory, Washington, D. C.

Thomas Edison (right) and George Eastman in 1928, trying out the new 16 mm Kodacolor Film

Bernhard Schmidt, Inventor of
the Schmidt camera

←

Yerkes Observatory Photo

James Lick, Founder of Lick
Observatory

→

Lick Observatory

THE·FOVR·FOOT·
SCHMIDT·PHOTOGRAPHIC·TELESCOPE·

Mount Wilson and Palomar Observatories

The 48-inch Schmidt telescope (Drawing by Russell W. Porter)

The Carnegie Astrograph at Lick Observatory

Alvan Clark sits by the 40-inch lens he made for the Yerkes Refractory Telescope,
as his assistant Carl Lundin prepares the glass for mounting.

Yerkes Observatory Photo

The 40-inch Yerkes refracting telescope

Lick Observatory Photo

The 36-inch refractor telescope at Lick Observatory

Mount Wilson and Palomar Observatories

The 100-inch Hooker telescope

Corning Glass Works

The mold into which molten glass was poured in casting the 200-inch telescope mirror for Mount Palomar. Metal rods melted during the pouring of the first disk; the second try was successful.

After cooling, the 200-inch disk was removed from its mold and preparations for the rail trip to California were begun.

The 200-inch disk was placed on a railroad flat car, firmly braced and protected by a metal sheath from the marksmanship of rural riflemen. This foresight proved valuable, for bullet pockmarks were found on the sheath upon arrival in California.

Dr. George Ellery Hale (From a watercolor drawing by his daughter)

Yerkes Observatory Photo

The 200-inch **Hale** telescope — sectional view through dome, with marginal identifications (Drawing by Russell W. Porter)

Mount Wilson and Palomar Observatories

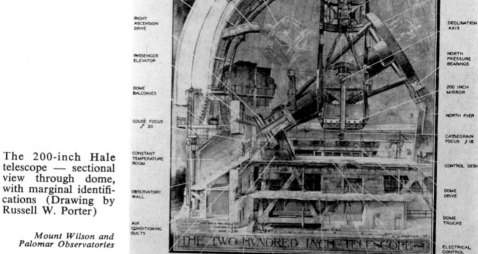

PHANTOM DRAWING SHOWING HOW THE OBSERVER GETS ON AND OFF THE TUBE

CRANE TRACK

TELESCOPE CAGE

PRIME FOCUS *f* 3.3

PRIME FOCUS PLATFORM

80 TON CRANE

DOME, 137 FEET DIAMETER

COUDÉ AND CASSEGRAIN MIRRORS

DOME SHUTTER 30 FT OPENING

HORSE SHOE, NORTH POLAR AXIS BEARING

RIGHT ASCENSION DRIVE

DECLINATION AXIS

PASSENGER ELEVATOR

NORTH PRESSURE BEARINGS

DOME BALCONIES

200 INCH MIRROR

COUDÉ FOCUS *f* 30

NORTH PIER

CONSTANT TEMPERATURE ROOM

CASSEGRAIN FOCUS *f* 16

CONTROL DESK

OBSERVATORY WALL

DOME DRIVE

AIR CONDITIONING DUCTS

DOME TRUCKS

SOUTH POLAR AXIS BEARING

ELECTRICAL CONTROL PANELS

SOUTH PIER   GROUND FLOOR   BASE FRAME SUPPORTS   MEZZANINE FLOOR   OFFICES   OBSERVATION FLOOR 5500 FT ABOVE SEA LEVEL

THE TWO HUNDRED INCH TELESCOPE

Model of 200-inch Mount Palomar telescope, cut from Balsa wood and cardboard, by Harry E. Neal, Jr. Model won first award in the sixth annual science fair, Bethesda-Chevy Chase High School, April, 1957.

The 200-inch Hale telescope dome with shutter open

Mount Wilson and Palomar Observatories

Backyard observator
and dome, built b
amateur Philip Lich
man, Washingtor
D. C.

Stuart Lichtma

Stuart Lichtman

The 8-inch Newtonian reflecting telescope made by Philip Lichtman. Small white tube (right) is 4-inch Lichtman-made f/10 refractor used as guide telescope; left, f/2.5 Aero-Ektar and 4-inch f/5 Zeiss Tessar for photography. Inventor machined all parts and installed mounting, drive and tracking mechanism himself.

The 50-foot "dish" of the Navy's radio telescope. Washington, D. C.

Official U. S. Navy Photo

Official U. S. Air Force Photo

Mounted on a 90 mm gun mount, this giant Telescopic Photographic Recorder is capable of tracking and photographing a pop bottle sized object four miles away.

Kay Gross, John Harper, Joel Gooch—
three Certified Junior Astronomers of the
Fort Worth, Texas, Children's Museum
astronomy class, using instruments from
the museum's lending library of telescopes.

W. D. Smith

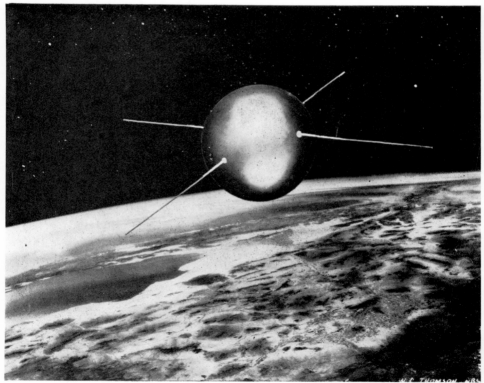

Official U. S. Navy Photo

Navy artist William C. Thompson, at the U. S. Naval Research Laboratory, depicts the flight
of the man-made "moon" over an area of 600,000 square miles. Photo taken from a Viking
12 at an altitude of 143.4 miles.

come world-renowned in the production of telescope mountings.

There are primarily two types of mountings—the *altazimuth* and the polar, or *equatorial*. The altazimuth mounting permits the telescope to be moved up and down (altitude) and right or left (azimuth), much the same as we move a camera on a tripod. The equatorial, however, is more complex.

The equatorial mounting is shaped roughly like a capital "T." The vertical bar is fastened to a base in such a way that the bar is parallel to the axis of the earth itself, and is called the *polar axis*. The crossbar is so arranged that it may rotate around the polar axis. The crossbar is known as the *declination axis*. The telescope is fixed to one end of the declination axis so that the instrument is parallel to the polar axis, and therefore also parallels the earth's axis (see Figure 8).

By means of a clock mechanism, the telescope on an equatorial mounting is rotated about the polar axis so that it counteracts the rotation of the earth. Thus the telescope may be pointed at a specific star and set in motion by its motor, and it will keep that star in fixed view.

The altazimuth mounting is satisfactory for the observer who sits and looks at the heavens through the telescope, but it is not practical for the photographing of celestial objects. The equatorial mounting, however, which remains focused on a star as the star appears to move, is admirably suited to the making of long photographic exposures necessary to get good celestial pictures.

Astronomical pictures were made possible by the combined discoveries of two Frenchmen, J. N. Niepce and Louis Jacques Mandé Daguerre. The "Daguerreotype" soon made it possible to bring the heavens down to earth.

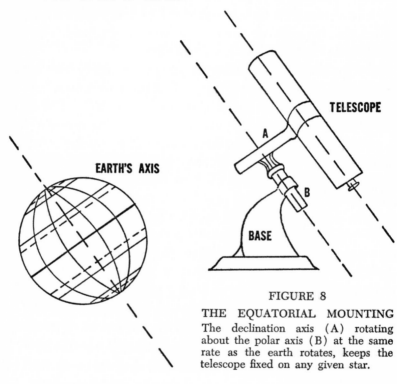

EARTH'S AXIS

TELESCOPE

A

B

BASE

FIGURE 8

THE EQUATORIAL MOUNTING
The declination axis (A) rotating about the polar axis (B) at the same rate as the earth rotates, keeps the telescope fixed on any given star.

CHAPTER SIX

A PLATE OF SKY

Surprise: Did you know that professional astronomers in our big observatories rarely look through their giant telescopes? It's true. Yet they actually "see" more celestial objects and farther into space than if they did so!

They let a camera do their stargazing. With a long exposure, a camera picks up light from stars which are much too faint to be seen with the eye, even through a telescope.

The discovery on which our modern photographic processes are based was made in 1835 by William Henry Fox Talbot, a British inventor. Some thirty-three years earlier, in 1802, two other Englishmen, Thomas Wedgwood and Sir Humphry Davy, coated paper with a solution of silver chloride, mounted it in a box, and cast shadows of peoples' profiles through an opening onto the paper. The shadowed area turned dark, making a perfect silhouette. The trouble was that the unshaded portion, when exposed to light, also turned just as dark. Talbot was the one who discovered how to overcome this difficulty.

Talbot made photographs with a *camera obscura,* a simple box with a convex lens at one end to transmit the image of some external object to sensitized paper or metal opposite the lens. Once the exposure was made, Talbot washed the exposed paper in a strong solution of ordinary salt, which dissolved the silver chloride on the areas that had not been struck by light. Thus the image itself remained.

Talbot's discovery was not practical because of the long time required for treating the paper and for exposing and processing the picture. Even as Talbot worked, however, two Frenchmen were also striving to make permanent pictures. They were Joseph Nicéphore Niepce, a scientist, and Louis Jacques Mandé Daguerre, a painter, who later invented the diorama. Both were working on the photographic problem separately when they formed a partnership in 1829 to pool their knowledge and skills.

They used silver plates coated with silver iodide. Although they could get an image, the subject still had to be exposed for a long period. One night Daguerre stored in a closet a plate which had been exposed for only a short time. In the closet were several chemicals, including a container of mercury. The next morning Daguerre was amazed to find a good clear image on the short-exposure plate. He discovered that vapor from the container of mercury had settled on the plate, thus "developing" it. This was the real beginning of the daguerreotype, which was an immediate success.

In 1839, Talbot made public his own method, which he called the "talbotype," or calotype process. Whereas Daguerre could make only one picture from one exposure, Talbot could make what Sir John Herschel called a "negative," and this could be used to make as many "positive" prints of a picture as desired.

Such were the beginnings of an art which was to revolutionize the use of telescopes and the science of astronomy.

There was no telegraph to flash word of Daguerre's discovery to the world, but the man who invented the telegraph, Samuel F. B. Morse, happened to be in France at the time, to obtain patents on his invention. Morse carried home as much information as he could get about the daguerreotype and passed it along to Dr. John W. Draper, an astronomer and professor of chemistry at New York University.

In 1840, Draper made a daguerreotype of his sister —probably the first photographic portrait. Soon, however, he sought other subjects for his camera, and chose the moon. At the point where his eye would normally make telescopic observations, Draper set up a photographic plate and pointed his telescope at the full moon. The plate was exposed for twenty minutes. When it was developed he held an image of the moon in his hands—an image about the size of a nickel, not too clear, but recognizable.

Other astronomers began to experiment with photography. In 1845, Armand Fizeau and Jean Foucault made the first successful daguerreotype of the sun. On July 17, 1850, William Cranch Bond, director of the Harvard Observatory, working with his son, George, and a photographer named J. A. Whipple, of Boston, made the first daguerreotype of a star (*Alpha Lyrae*), using the observatory's 15-inch refracting telescope.

In 1851 an English architect named Scott Archer invented the "wet collodion" process, in which glass plates were coated with collodion sensitized with silver nitrate. The plates had to be used while wet and had to be developed immediately, but the exposure time was only about ten seconds, as compared to three minutes for Talbot's calotype and thirty minutes or more for the daguerreotype. In 1864 a collodion emulsion was developed by B. J. Sayce and W. B. Bolton, giving greater sensitivity but no faster speed. For the next several years a number of men experimented with a gelatine emulsion which was finally introduced commercially in 1877 and which required exposures ranging from one two-hundredth of a second to a full second.

The fast exposures made it possible to get better astronomical pictures, but the glass plates were cumbersome and fragile. In 1884, William H. Walker invented a film roll, using sensitized paper instead of glass. A year later George Eastman, of Kodak fame, patented a machine for coating sensitized paper in long rolls.

George Eastman, born July 12, 1854, in Waterville, New York, was a shining example of the rags-to-riches hero. Compelled by poverty to leave school at fourteen, he found a three-dollar-a-week job as a messenger-janitor. His mother took boarders, and George studied accounting at night. When he was twenty he became a bank clerk in Rochester, New York, at $800 a year. From this salary he managed to save $3,000 during the next seven years.

Some of his earnings he invested in a camera and equipment. He found it so unwieldy and difficult to use that he began experimenting at home to simplify the process. He studied all the printed material at hand, and after three years of hard work he decided to rent space in Rochester to manufacture dry plates, which he did successfully. When the sensitized paper was introduced, Eastman produced a new kind of picturemaker. The first Kodak camera was born in June, 1888.

The Kodak held a paper roll for 100 exposures and cost $25, fully loaded. When the exposures were completed, the owner returned the camera, unopened, to Eastman at Rochester, where the paper was developed and printed and a fresh roll inserted for ten dollars.

In August, 1889, Eastman (then called the Eastman Dry Plate and Film Company) developed the first rolls of transparent film. Two years later he made it possible to load the film in daylight, and in 1900 he marketed the first "Brownie" box camera. Cost: One dollar. Suddenly anyone could be a photographer by pushing a lever.

Today the Eastman Kodak Company makes high-speed film and special equipment for virtually all scientific fields, including astronomical photography. It publishes books and pamphlets on every phase of picturemaking. One of these, *Photography in Astronomy*, by E. W. H. Selwyn of the Kodak Research Laboratories in Harrow, England, describes in detail many of the celestial objects photographed, and the methods and instruments used. It is probably of more value to the professional astronomer than to the beginner. Such a book could not have been written if it were not for those pioneers who captured the first celestial pictures on plate or film—pioneers like Warren de la Rue, for example.

De la Rue was born January 18, 1815, on the island of Guernsey, and as a youth he became deeply interested in astronomy. When he was thirty-five years old he made a 13-inch reflector with which he made careful studies of many stellar bodies. For some time he made drawings of these objects, but at the Great Exhibition of 1851 in London he visited a display where he saw a daguerreotype of the moon, made by George P. Bond. De la Rue abandoned his drawings for photographs, and with wet collodion plates he produced some of the finest pictures of the moon ever made.

In 1854, de la Rue turned his attention and his camera to the sun. His work in solar photography brought him a commission from the Royal Society in 1857 to make some kind of a device that could be installed in Kew Observatory to make frequent observations of the sun. As a result, he invented the "photoheliograph"—a four-foot refracting telescope so arranged that a plateholder could be attached to the eyepiece. On this holder the plate itself was covered by a spring-operated screen, or slide. When pointed at the sun and triggered, the slide uncovered the plate just long enough to catch the sun's image on it.

De la Rue's photoheliograph produced the first solar pictures with any real scientific value, and was used successfully at Kew Observatory until 1872, when it was moved to Greenwich Observatory and used for another ten years.

An astronomical giant step was taken when the telescope and camera were combined with the spectroscope to analyze the substances of which the moon, sun, planets and stars were made. Sir Isaac Newton, in 1666, cut a slit in a window shutter so that a streak of sunlight would pass through a prism (a clear glass triangular block). The single ray of light, after it passed through the glass, revealed the colors of the rainbow, much as we see colors sparkle on a diamond ring in the sunlight. Newton correctly concluded that white light, or sunlight, is actually a combination of the seven major colors: red, orange, yellow, green, blue, indigo, and violet.

In 1802, William H. Wollaston, an English chemist who lived a hermitlike existence, also cut a slit in a windowblind and let a crack of sunshine touch a prism. In the resulting separation of the colored rays (the *spectrum*) he noticed that there were some dark lines, but he did not attach any special significance to them at the time. It remained for Joseph von Fraunhofer, the lens wizard, to open a new door to celestial exploration with the spectroscope.

In 1814, Fraunhofer set up a slit and a prism in front of a telescope, thus devising the first spectroscope. Later a man named W. H. Simms placed a lens in front of the prism to "collimate" (straighten out) the light. Fraunhofer charted thousands of lines in the spectrum, including the dark bands, and identified each line by a letter, or by a letter and number combined. These lines in the spectrum are still known as the "Fraunhofer lines."

Fraunhofer puzzled over their significance until he died, and it was more than forty years later, in 1859, that another German physicist, Gustav Robert Kirchhoff, discovered that the bands of the spectrum were clues to the types of substances from which the various colors came.

Kirchhoff worked in the laboratory of Robert W. Bunsen, inventor of the Bunsen burner. Using this device, Kirchhoff discovered that the dark lines marked "D" on Fraunhofer's chart could be changed to bright lines by placing a yellow sodium flame in front of the spectroscopic slit. Therefore, he reasoned, sodium could be identified by the color of its flame in the spectroscope. This meant that the other colors in sunlight would reveal the nature of the elements of which the sun itself was made.

The "Fraunhofer lines" were thus keyed to the elements which produced them. D_1 and D_2 represent sodium, as we have seen. E is iron, F is hydrogen, A is oxygen, and so on.

A London astronomer, William Huggins, combined the camera with the spectroscope. Huggins used one of the first 8-inch telescopes made by Alvan Clark. In his private observatory, working with Professor W. A. Miller, Huggins was the first to analyze a star by using Kirchhoff's discovery. In 1863 he tried to photograph the spectrum, but the wet collodion plates then in use required too long an exposure to be practical. In 1875, however, when the faster gelatin process appeared, Huggins made successful spectroscopic pictures. The combination of prism, telescope and camera is called the spectrograph. It is in world-wide use today, and with it the scientific world has uncovered countless secrets of the skies.

An important outgrowth of the spectrograph was the "spectroheliograph," developed in 1890 by twenty-one-year-old George Ellery Hale, first director of the Mount Wilson Observatory and one of the great American astronomers. The spectroheliograph makes it possible to learn the specific areas occupied by the various substances in the sun. The method is quite simple. The sunlight comes through a slit, to a lens, to a prism, which divides it into the spectrum. Then, however, another slit is used behind a lens on the other side of the prism to capture any *one* of the light bands. This band would come from only one substance on the sun. The single color band penetrates the slit and strikes a photographic plate. Since the slit will not admit wave lengths except the one selected, no other bands register on the plate.

When the whole device is moved in front of the plate, it builds up a picture of the sun in such a way that the single substance is the only one identified in the image (see Figure 9). Thus its position on the sun can easily be fixed, as can its motion. Sunspots, for instance, are really gigantic storms ringed by flaming swirls of hydrogen gas shooting thousands of miles into space. Photographically these whirling areas remind us of the "pinwheels" we used to set off on the

Fourth of July, except that some of the spots are so huge that the earth could be dropped into their centers without touching the edges!

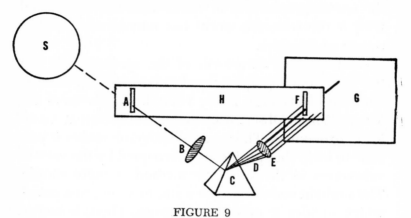

FIGURE 9

BASIC SPECTROHELIOGRAPH

Sun (S) casts its light through narrow Source Slit (A) and collimating lens (B) to prism (C), where it divides into spectrum (D). Rays enter telescope objective (E), and single band of spectrum penetrates Second Slit (F) to register on photographic plate (G). By moving entire device (H) to cover remaining areas of sun's image, distribution of source element on sun can be established.

As this is written, scientists are optimistic about a new device which will revolutionize astronomical photography and also may let them see much farther into space than heretofore. Dr. E. J. Sternglass and Mr. Milton M. Wachtel, research physicists in the Electronics and Nuclear Physics Department of the Westinghouse Research Laboratories in Pittsburgh, Pennsylvania, have developed an "image amplifier," or "image multiplier" in the form of a small electronic tube about three inches long.

Purpose of the multiplier is to make dim images much brighter. Basically it would achieve two things —it would improve the present range of telescopes and also would permit astronomical photographs to be made at very fast exposures.

When perfected, if the multiplier were attached to the 200-inch telescope at Mount Palomar, it is expected that star images now seen only faintly would be 10,000 to 20,000 times brighter! Some which are now invisible will be seen for the first time.

Photographs of planets now require exposures ranging from one-tenth to one-half of a second. Because of turbulence in the earth's atmosphere, these relatively long exposures produce blurred images, even of bright planets. With the image multiplier, however, it may be possible to snap pictures in one five-hundredth of a second, "freezing" the planet by overcoming any blur due to "dancing" caused by atmospheric disturbances.

Dr. John S. Hall, head of the Equatorial Division of the U.S. Naval Observatory, is a member of a Joint Committee on Image Tubes for Telescopes, of the Carnegie Institution of Washington, and, with Dr. W. A. Baum of the Mount Wilson and Palomar observatories, he has made tests of a few early models of image-multiplier tubes, using the 26-inch refractor at the Naval Observatory.

Under Dr. Hall's direction, a more practical laboratory test was devised, leading to further experiments by him and his associates with the Navy's 40-inch reflector at Flagstaff, Arizona. The research continues.

Dr. Hall, who became interested in astronomy when he was only thirteen, and who is today one of the ranking astronomers of the world, is convinced that the image multiplier will be perfected and that it will represent one of the most tremendous astronomical advances in history.

Just as the early makers of reflecting telescopes had trouble with aberration, so did the astronomical photographers have trouble with two new reflector problems—coma and astigmatism. In photographing the stars they found that the images near the outer edges of the negative were slightly streamlined, like comets, when they should have been perfectly round. The reason for this was that the light from these stars fell upon the telescope mirror at a sharp angle, whereas those directly in front of the mirror photographed satisfactorily. The slanting rays simply would not focus properly because of the curvature of the mirror. This is known as coma.

Astigmatism is defined as a defect of a lens "whereby rays of light from an external point fail to converge to a focus, thus giving rise to imperfect vision or images." In astronomical photography, astigmatism makes star images at the very edge of the negative appear to be oval-shaped instead of round.

The problem of coma was generally solved about 1905 when a German astronomer, Conrad Schwarzschild, proposed that another mirror be added to the reflecting telescope, curved in such a way that it would offset any distortion produced by the main glass. Not until 1930, however, was a reflecting telescope designed for photographic use which eliminated both coma and astigmatism. This was the famous invention of an Estonian named Bernhard Schmidt, and although it is a telescope it is known as the Schmidt Camera, since it can be used only for photographic purposes. (Other types of lens-and-mirror combinations are designed for visual observations.)

Bernhard Schmidt was a one-armed astronomer who made his living for some twenty-five years by grinding and polishing lenses and reflectors for other astronomers. This work is hard enough for a man with two hands. For Schmidt, working only with his left hand, it would seem a strange occupation for a livelihood. Schmidt was starry-eyed from the time he was old enough to walk. As a boy he made a telescope lens from the thick bottom of an old bottle. Having no abrasive material, he gathered some clean sand from a beach, placed it in a saucer, and rubbed the bottle against it to shape his lens.

As a youthful how-to-do-it addict, Schmidt dabbled in many fields, one of which was the making of gunpowder. As part of an experiment he placed some of his powder in an iron pipe, tamping it in tightly. He knew the powder would ignite if lighted, but he did not realize that he had actually made an effective and dangerous bomb. On a Sunday when his family went to church, Schmidt touched a match to the powder. There was an earsplitting crash as the bomb exploded, taking with it the boy's right forearm.

Schmidt went on to study engineering and became an expert on lenses, mirrors, telescopes and cameras.

Because of his optical skills he was invited to live and work at the Bergedorf Observatory in 1926, and it was there that he conceived the Schmidt Camera which is now in world-wide astronomical use.

In the Schmidt device, the telescope receives the image on a concave reflector which is spherical (not parabolic) in shape. Between this mirror and the end of the instrument is a "correcting lens" which bends the incoming light rays so that those which would otherwise slant become parallel with others before they reach the mirror. In this way, all the rays are properly focused.

Facing the mirror is the photographic plate, upon which is captured the reflected (and corrected) image. But because the mirror is spherical, the photographic film is fitted over a form which is correspondingly spherical. This avoids the distortion which would be created if a flat film were used to photograph the spherical mirror.

Bernhard Schmidt died in 1935, but his invention was destined to be used by astronomers in observatories throughout the world. One of the first of the great mountain observatories in the United States was Lick Observatory at Mount Hamilton, California—the tomb with a telescope.

CHAPTER SEVEN

TOMB WITH A TELESCOPE

A ragged, unkempt millionaire gave $700,000 to buy a mountain, erect an observatory, and to make a telescope "superior to and more powerful than any telescope yet made. . . ." From this bequest came Lick Observatory, named for James Lick. He never saw the telescope, he had no interest in astronomy, and no one today knows the reason for his gift, unless it was that he believed the observatory would be an enduring monument to perpetuate his name.

James Lick was born August 21, 1796, in Fredericksburg, Pennsylvania. He had very little formal schooling, but served an apprenticeship as a carpenter and joiner, and when he was about nineteen he left home to go to Baltimore, Maryland, to work for a piano manufacturer named Joseph Hiskey.

Lick learned his trade well, because when he was only twenty-four he sailed for South America, where he began his own business of making pianos and organs. He lived in Buenos Aires, Argentina, in Valparaiso, Chile, and in Lima, Peru, and stayed in South America for seventeen years. In 1847, shortly before gold was discovered in California, Lick arrived in San

Francisco with a small fortune of $30,000 in gold doubloons.

In 1848 he used part of this money to buy land in the Santa Clara Valley, on the shores of Lake Tahoe, and on Catalina Island. Often dressing in threadbare clothes, extremely careless about his personal appearance, including his bushy beard and wavy dark hair, Lick soon earned a reputation as an eccentric miser. One of his eccentricities was a flour mill which he built at Alviso, near San Jose. The mill was constructed of solid mahogany, walnut, and other expensive woods ordinarily used in the building of costly mansions, yet he paid his workmen as little as possible and begrudged the spending of money for ordinary comforts for himself.

While the mill was under construction, Lick was approached by a group of educators who appealed to him to contribute some of his money to set up a unit for scientific research at the University of California. Lick listened calmly to their plea, and just as calmly told them he was not interested in contributing a dime to any such cause.

Gradually his investments and his fortune grew, and he built an elegantly appointed San Francisco hotel called "The Lick House," which eventually became his home. For twenty years, however, he lived alone in apparent poverty in the Santa Clara Valley.

When Lick died on October 1, 1876, his estate totaled three million dollars! His will indicated that he had given considerable thought to the disposition of this fortune. Although he had never married, he bequeathed $150,000 to an illegitimate son, and virtually all the rest of the money went to public benefactions.

For example, he gave $150,000 for the building and maintenance of free public baths in San Francisco; $540,000 to create "The California School of Mechanic Arts" (a manual training school for boys and girls); $100,000 for the building of bronze statues in front of the San Francisco City Hall, representing three periods in California history; $100,000 for a Home for Old Ladies in San Francisco; and $60,000 for a statue in Golden Gate Park as a memorial to Francis Scott Key, author of "The Star-Spangled Banner." He had already committed $700,000 "for the purpose of purchasing land . . . and putting up on such land . . . a powerful telescope, superior to and more powerful than any telescope yet made . . . and also a suitable observatory connected therewith . . . and the said telescope and observatory are to be known as the Lick Astronomical Department of the University of California."

This last bequest was made only because of a quirk in Lick's thinking. He wanted to build some spectacular monument to his own memory—some gigantic structure which would strike the imagination and keep the name of Lick alive long after its owner had departed. What greater, more enduring monument could he build than a pyramid? It would be fashioned after the massive pyramid of Cheops in Gizeh, which covers some thirteen acres and stands more than 480 feet

99

high. But Lick's pyramid would be made with blocks of gleaming marble and would rise majestically on the shores of San Francisco Bay!

While this stupendous project was taking form in Lick's eccentric mind, it occurred to him that a marble pyramid on San Francisco Bay would be especially vulnerable to cannon shot in the event of a war. And if, perchance, the pyramid should be blown to smithereens in such a war, it was not likely that others would attempt to rebuild it. In that event, the Lick monument would be no monument at all.

"The observatory took the place of the pyramid," said Edward S. Holden, late director of the Lick Observatory.

Before his death, Lick spent considerable time in selecting a site for the telescope, investigating possible locations at Lake Tahoe and St. Helena. In August, 1875, acting upon a suggestion made by his "confidential agent," Thomas E. Fraser, he chose Mount Hamilton, rising 4,200 feet above sea level, but the mountain was not easily accessible and his choice was made on condition that Santa Clara County officials would build a first-class road to the summit. The county agreed.

The first supplies hauled to the mountaintop came from San Jose, about nineteen miles away, and the trip over the rough trail took five days. Lick himself never climbed the mountain, and he died about two months before the county completed the road, which has 365 curves in its final five miles. Cost of the road: $78,000.

His choice of Mount Hamilton would have pleased Sir Isaac Newton, who once suggested that telescopes set up on high places would give more satisfactory results than those on low ground. "For the air through which we look upon the stars is in a perpetual tremor," Newton wrote, "as may be seen by the tremulous motion of shadows cast from high towers and by the twinkling of fix'd stars. . . . The only remedy is a most serene and quiet air such as may perhaps be found on the tops of the highest mountains above the grosser clouds."

Building of the observatory was supervised by a Board of Lick Trustees headed by Captain R. S. Floyd, a wealthy sometime-skipper of a Pacific steamer. Floyd traveled to observatories in the United States and Europe, interviewing astronomers and telescope makers to get the best advice about equipment for the observatory. He finally chose two famous astronomers, Professor Simon Newcomb and Professor Edward S. Holden, to be responsible for the general plan of the buildings and the equipment.

The professors invited S. W. Burnham, famed for his discoveries and measurements of close double stars, to make atmospheric tests on Mount Hamilton. In 1879, Burnham brought a 6-inch telescope there and spent two months on the summit. He concluded that the location offered "advantages superior to those found at any point where a permanent observatory has been established." Accordingly, the building of the observatory began in 1880 under the general supervision of Captain Floyd and his chief assistant,

Thomas Fraser, who had recommended the site to Lick.

Fraser, a carpenter from Nova Scotia, told the workmen, "We must have the best here, and I will never submit to anything else while I am in charge!"

For eight rugged years Floyd and Fraser worked to build the observatory. To level off the 3,300-acre mountaintop, they blasted away more than 40,000 tons of rock, all of which had to be removed by hand. From nearby springs a water supply was developed with a steam engine to lift water into tanks situated on a peak east of the observatory. About a mile from the summit was a clay deposit where the bricks for the building were baked. The iron pier and mounting for the telescope were made by Warner and Swasey and weighed some thirty-seven tons. They were hauled by horse or mule team and lifted into position with crude mechanical devices. Mules also hauled up the materials for the dome, seventy-five feet in diameter, weighing about ninety tons, built by the Union Iron Works of San Francisco.

All this was designed to house, at Lick's direction, a telescope more powerful than any yet made. However, six years before the completion of what was then to be the world's largest telescope, a wealthy amateur astronomer, Dr. Henry Draper of New York, provided the observatory with his own 12-inch refractor, an instrument still in use there. At the time the 12-inch was installed, King Kalakaua of the Hawaiian Islands happened to be visiting the observatory, and he was the first visitor to look through this instrument.

In the years before its completion, the observatory was a favorite tourist attraction. Although it was reached only by a five-hour journey from San Jose in horse-drawn stagecoaches, some five thousand people made the trip every year to see the building and to look through the 12-inch telescope, said to have one of the finest lenses ever made by Alvan Clark.

After the Lick trustees checked on virtually every telescope maker in the world, they chose Alvan Clark and Sons to grind and polish the crown and flint lenses for the 36-inch glass monument to James Lick. The glass disks for the lenses were cast by Feil and Son of Paris, but it took this firm five years to produce castings with the degree of perfection needed for the three-foot lens. Another whole year was devoted to the grinding and polishing by the Clarks. In December, 1886, the lens was placed aboard a special railroad car to travel across the United States. To protect it went sixteen people, including Alvan G. Clark, who remained until 1888, when the fifty-six-foot tube, weighing some three tons, was installed, and the observatory was formally turned over to the regents of the University of California.

The new observatory was equipped with an unusual feature which was to set the pattern for similar modern institutions. The entire floor of the building was made so that it could be raised sixteen and a half feet, elevatorwise. This not only simplified the movement of the telescope, but also made it possible for the observer to maintain a comfortable position and to work at the eyepiece.

One junior astronomer of the observatory's original staff was Edward E. Barnard, who was born in Nashville, Tennessee, in 1857. Barnard's early life was a struggle for existence. When he was only eight years old he went to work for a Nashville photographer, getting what formal schooling he could as time permitted. A book on astronomy and a small spyglass in the photographic studio aroused his interest in telescopes, and when he was twenty he made a telescope with which he began a search for comets.

Devoting his spare time to a study of the heavens, he also studied other subjects in schools and finally won a diploma from Vanderbilt University when he was thirty years old. By that time he had become widely known in astronomical circles and in 1887 he was offered the post of junior astronomer at Lick.

At the observatory Barnard did pioneer work in the measurement of planets and asteroids (small, irregularly shaped planets). He photographed many comets, eventually accumulating an invaluable collection of some 1,400 comet negatives. In addition he discovered sixteen new comets and a fifth moon of Jupiter, and he proved by a series of photographs that the dark, seemingly open spaces in the Milky Way are actually "dark nebulae" or clouds of celestial dust.

Barnard worked frequently with a 6-inch telescope, a midget compared to the 36-inch refractor, yet a giant considering the results he obtained. The 36-inch instrument, however, has fulfilled its every expectation. It has been used to make both visual and photographic observations of planets, satellites, meteors, and double stars (more than 5,000 of these have been discovered at Lick). It has revealed more than thirty new comets. Precise positions of thousands of stars have been established. Photographs of the sun and moon have helped scientists learn more about these bodies, and have also been valuable in making a detailed moon map. The study of variable stars (stars which fluctuate in brightness) forms an integral part of the Lick research program.

One of the most important uses of the great telescope has been made in combination with the spectroscope. The target: To learn how fast our solar system is moving. Answer: About twelve miles per second, toward the constellation Hercules. The whole universe, say the Lick experts, appears to be expanding (flying away from us) at thousands of miles per second.

Since the opening of the observatory it has added considerable equipment. In 1895 it acquired from England a 36-inch reflector made by A. A. Common, who sold it originally to Edward Crossley of Halifax, England. The British climate made observations useless, and Crossley presented the instrument to Lick Observatory. J. E. Keeler, then director of the institution, used the reflector to make the finest photographs of nebulae that had been taken to that time. He discovered hundreds of spiral nebulae and predicted correctly that thousands more could be pictured with the Crossley. In 1934 the silvered surface, which had to be renewed each year, was replaced by a thin film of aluminum, which lasts at least five years and reflects much more ultraviolet light than the silver. This was the first large astronomical reflector to have an aluminized mirror.

Another Lick instrument is a 20-inch astrograph. "This," say the observatory officials, "is in reality a giant camera, designed specifically for taking stellar photographs that can be measured with high precision." Here again, the astrograph mounting was made by the Warner and Swasey Company. The lens is 20 inches in diameter, the instrument about 12 feet long. It was the gift of the Carnegie Corporation, and its main function is to furnish two complete sets of pictures taken several years apart. Scientists believe that an accurate comparison of these two series will give them valuable information about the rotation and internal motions of our Milky Way system, called the *Galaxy*. The first series of plates, consisting of 1,246 exposures of two hours each, was begun in 1947 and finished in 1954. The second series will begin about 1960.

The latest and greatest telescope at Lick is a 120-inch reflector which cost about $2,500,000—four times the sum spent for the original buildings and instruments. This is the second largest reflecting telescope in the world today. The mirror and its supports weigh about ten tons. The mounting was designed by W. W. Baustian, an engineer from the California Institute of Technology, and erected by the Hudson Pacific-Murphy Corporation of Emeryville, California. Its moving parts weigh 150 tons, yet they are floated on a film of oil under high pressure to give ease of motion as the telescope moves to follow the stars. All optical processing was done in the observatory's basement optical shops.

Movement of the telescope may be controlled either from a fixed console on the floor or from the several observing stations. One of these is at the *prime focus,* at the upper end of the telescope tube, some seventy feet above the floor.

Another observing station is known as the coudé focus. Oddly enough, this station is in a room below the main floor. The light from the 120-inch mirror is reflected by other mirrors to the coudé room, where it can be photographed.

Besides the major telescopes, the Lick Observatory has a 22-inch Tauchmann reflector, a dome for small astrographic cameras, numerous measuring devices, and astronomical clocks. It also maintains an astronomical library of some 25,000 volumes, one of the world's best.

The 36-inch telescope at Lick Observatory is still used on every clear night of the year. No formal courses are taught at Mount Hamilton, but advanced graduate students may gain observatory experience and do research under the direction of the observatory staff. Visiting astronomers may also use the equipment for investigating special problems. The public is admitted by ticket only, and tickets may be obtained free by writing to the Lick Observatory, Mount Hamilton, California. Average yearly attendance is about 35,000.

In addition to the celestial marvels, the visitor to

the observatory will see an earthly tablet on the base of the 36-inch refractor bearing the simple inscription: "Here lies the body of James Lick." When alive, Lick had often suggested that he might be buried near the observatory. Originally buried in a cemetery at Lone Mountain, Lick's remains were later moved to the base of the great telescope, which thus became his tomb and his gravestone.

Perhaps James Lick, with his penchant for memorials and his order for the world's most powerful telescope, would be disappointed to learn that the 36-inch instrument was the world's largest refractor for only ten short years. In 1897, in Williams Bay, Wisconsin, astronomers prepared to look at the skies through a 40-inch telescope—four inches greater in diameter than the Lick instrument, and still the world's largest refractor. This was the beginning of another great American scientific institution, the Yerkes Observatory of the University of Chicago. It was also a milestone in the exciting career of one of the most renowned American astronomers of all time, Dr. George Ellery Hale.

CHAPTER EIGHT

MAN ON A MOUNTAINTOP

When fourteen-year-old George Ellery Hale mounted a telescope on the roof of his house in Chicago, Illinois, and looked skyward, he knew that he was gazing at his own future.

"I cannot fix the date of my first interest in astronomy," Hale wrote later, "but it must have been when I was 13 or 14 years old. I built a telescope, but as I used a large single lens the images were not good. About this time I became acquainted with S. W. Burnham, then a stenographer in the Chicago law courts by day, and an ardent observer of double stars by night. Through him I learned of a second-hand Clark refractor of four inches aperture. This was purchased by my father, and I mounted it on the roof of our house. The astonishing views it afforded of Saturn, the moon, Jupiter, and other objects, excited an intense desire to carry on actual research. So I attached a plate-holder to the telescope and photographed a partial eclipse of the sun. I also began to observe sunspots and made drawings of them. Thus I became an amateur astronomer."

Throughout Hale's life the sun held a peculiar fascination for him. As a youth he made a spectroscope. "Nothing," he said, "could exceed my enthusiasm in observing the solar spectrum and in measuring the principal lines. I bought Lockyer's *Studies in Spectrum Analysis,* and began the observation of flame and spark spectra and their comparison with the spectrum of the sun. At last I had found my true course and I have held to it ever since."

Born June 29, 1868, in Chicago, Hale attended the public schools and Allen Academy there, later majoring in mathematics, physics and chemistry at the Massachusetts Institute of Technology. He volunteered his services at the Harvard Observatory and there developed the first form of his spectroheliograph.

Little by little, Hale built a private observatory at his home, called it Kenwood Observatory, and with his own hands made some of the instruments used in it.

Graduating from M.I.T. in 1890, he soon married Miss Evelina Conklin, and the couple went west on their honeymoon. During this trip they visited the Lick Observatory, where Hale was visibly impressed by the 36-inch refractor. This visit was to have great significance later.

In 1891 the twenty-three-year-old stargazer went to Europe and studied the methods and equipment of noted astronomers and spectroscopists. In 1892 he was appointed Associate Professor of Astrophysics at the University of Chicago, and the following winter he took a course in thermodynamics and theories of radiation at the University of Berlin in Germany.

The memorable sights he had seen through the 36-inch refractor at Lick remained vivid in Hale's mind. In August, 1892, during a social visit with his friend, Alvan Clark, Hale's ears perked up at a yarn which Clark told about the Lick instrument. According to Clark, a group of Los Angeles businessmen, jealous of the publicity given to Mount Hamilton and the 36-inch refractor, promoted a fund to buy a 40-inch telescope which would make Lick the *second* largest in the world. The 40-inch objective was ordered from Alvan Clark—then the bottom fell out of the Los Angeles real estate boom, and the telescope deal fell with it.

Clark lamented the fact that he had obtained the glass disks for the lens from Mantois in Paris, and that there was now no reason to grind and polish them, or to install them even if they were completed.

Promptly Hale took the story to W. R. Harper, president of the University of Chicago, and together they called on Mr. Charles T. Yerkes, a Chicago industrialist, to ask if he would finance the making of a 40-inch telescope. He would and did. Alvan Clark completed the lens for $66,000, and Yerkes also paid $55,000 for the Warner and Swasey mounting, and $195,000 for the building of the Yerkes Observatory (now covering eighty acres) at Williams Bay, Wisconsin.

The observatory was completed in 1897 and Hale

111

was named its first director and also Professor of Astrophysics at the University of Chicago. He was then twenty-nine years old.

The Yerkes Observatory is seventy-six miles from Chicago and 1,050 feet above sea level, on Lake Geneva, Wisconsin. Its 40-inch refractor is in constant use. Its chief advantages are its light-gathering power (about 35,000 times greater than that of the unaided eye) and its magnifying power. Theoretically the 40-inch telescope can magnify an object by 4,000 diameters. Atmospheric conditions, however, are never good enough to allow the use of such high magnification, and powers of more than 1,000 diameters are rarely used.

The telescope tube is 63 feet long and weighs six tons. It is moved by motors built to such precision that they can move the tube one one-hundredth of an inch and stop it at a desired position.

The observatory dome, also made by Warner and Swasey, is ninety feet across. It can be rotated on twenty-six wheels by an electric motor and can make one complete revolution in six minutes. The slit, or opening through which the telescope points at the sky, is eleven feet wide. The thirty-seven-and-one-half-ton floor (Warner and Swasey) rises twenty-three feet. As in other observatories, the dome is never heated because heat waves through the open shutter would distort the images.

The telescope is used for observing stars on every clear night, and the sun on many clear days. An important method of using the telescope with a camera was developed in 1900 by George Willis Ritchey who, like Hale, became interested in astronomy as a boy. Ritchey designed color filters and a special plateholder which would follow slight oscillations of celestial objects caused by unsteady atmosphere, thus producing sharper pictures. Ritchey's photographs of the moon, star clusters and nebulae are among the best in existence. His ability won him an appointment as superintendent of instrument design at Yerkes and a post as assistant professor of astronomy at the University of Chicago.

The big telescope has been used to measure the positions of stars in star clusters, the fainter satellites of our solar system, nebulae, and faint comets. Thousands of pictures which have been taken to determine the distances of certain stars from the sun are becoming more valuable because, with the lapse of time, new pictures of the same stars will reveal more about their motions and the laws governing those motions.

About one half of the night hours with the telescope are devoted to spectroscopic work, in which the experts have used a star spectroscope made by John A. Brashear. It was discovered that a photograph of the spectrum of a star, accompanied on the same plate by a comparison spectrum of a spark between metal terminals, may be measured under a microscope. By this method it was found that the average star moves about ten miles per second, and that the hotter stars tend to move away from the sun. More than 25,000 spectrograms have been obtained at the Yerkes Observatory, and investigations are now under way to determine the physical properties and the chemical ingredients of the atmospheres of the stars.

Another important use of the 40-inch refractor has been the continuing study of the sun with the spectroheliograph, invented by George Ellery Hale.

Hale's genius was recognized by the Carnegie Institution of Washington, which invited him to serve on a committee to inspect sites for another proposed observatory. In 1903, Hale made his first trip to Mount Wilson, near Pasadena, California, to visit a friend, Professor W. J. Hussey of Lick Observatory, also a member of the committee. Hussey was still making his inspection of the mountain as a possible site. Hale, however, lugged a 3¼-inch telescope up the rough mountain trail and made actual observations at the summit for several months. Based on these observations he recommended that the Carnegie Institution finance an expedition from the Yerkes Observatory and the installation of a heliostat (a horizontal telescope for observing the sun). The Institution agreed and informally appointed Hale as Director of the Mount Wilson Observatory.

After making careful observations for a year, Hale and his associates reported to the Carnegie Institution that Mount Wilson would make an ideal site for an independent observatory. Although Hale realized that technical difficulties made it quite impossible to build a refracting telescope with a lens larger than the 40-inch glass at Yerkes, he was convinced that bigger *reflecting* telescopes could be made and would reveal new celestial secrets.

George Ritchey, while at Yerkes, had begun work on a 60-inch mirror which had been bought for Hale by his father. Its completion was delayed for lack of money. Hale placed Ritchey in charge of the optical shops at Mount Wilson, where Ritchey finished the mirror and designed the building and dome where it is used today.

Although the 60-inch mirror could range farther into space than any other instrument, it was not big enough for Hale. In 1906 he talked with John D. Hooker, a wealthy Los Angeles businessman interested in astronomy, about financing the building of an 84-inch reflector for Mount Wilson. Hooker liked the idea and agreed to put up the money for the mirror. In fact he became so enthusiastic that before the order was placed for the glass, Hooker volunteered to invest a larger sum for a 100-inch mirror—the largest ever made, to that time.

Dr. Hale was delighted, but there was one hitch. John Hooker would pay for the mirror, but a mounting and an observatory building for so huge an instrument would cost half a million dollars, which Mr. Hooker was not in a position to spend. The project was suddenly threatened by this lack of money.

In 1910, Andrew Carnegie himself visited Mount Wilson, where he inspected the equipment and squinted through the telescopes as eagerly as would any curious sightseer. Hale told him about Mr. Hooker's offer. Carnegie wanted the Carnegie Institution of Washington to finance the mounting and observatory, but he discovered that the Institution must use its entire income to maintain its other nine research departments. Once again the gleam faded from Dr. Hale's hopeful eyes.

In 1911, Hale set out for Egypt to carry on some stellar research. While stopping in Italy he bought an American newspaper and read an article in it which made him want to shout with glee. Andrew Carnegie, the story said, had presented another ten million dollars to the Carnegie Institution. In a letter to the trustees, Carnegie wrote, "I hope the work at Mount Wilson will be vigorously pushed, because I am so anxious to hear the expected results from it. I should like to be satisfied, before I depart, that we are going to repay to the old land some part of the debt we owe . . . by revealing more clearly than ever . . . the new heavens."

Hale came home and work on the new giant began promptly. The 100-inch mirror was cast at the St. Gobain Glass Works in France and shipped to Pasadena to be ground, polished, and figured, a task which required six whole years of painstaking labor by George Ritchey and two assistants whom he had trained. The finished mirror was 13 inches thick, weighed four and one-half tons. It was given a coating of silver, later changed to aluminum, and was eventually sheathed in cork insulation to minimize the effects of possible changes in the observatory temperature. When the mirror has to be resilvered it is lowered on a hydraulic lift to a laboratory underneath the observatory floor, where the work is done.

On the night of November 1, 1917, the great telescope was ready for its first test. Hard work, long
hours, and endless experimenting and computing had
taken their toll from Dr. Hale. Although his health
was poor he came to the observatory that night with
Alfred Noyes, the English poet, who was visiting
California. Together they met Walter S. Adams,
Hale's right-hand man (who later followed Hale as
director of the observatory). Hale was anxious to look
through the telescope.

"Don't build your hopes too high," Adams told him.
"George Ritchey thinks the mirror has what he calls
a strong and a weak diameter. He thinks it changes
figure when it changes position."

Hale suggested that Ritchey's fears might be due
to atmospheric and other conditions in the hall where
the mirror was originally tested. Adams agreed, and
at dusk they went with Noyes to the huge dome in
the hope that they would see farther into space than
any man had yet seen.

There it stood, dwarfing the men, a giant finger
pointing up at the skies it was designed to probe. To
get some idea of the power of this huge eye, compare
it with your own. The pupil of a human eye is about
one fifth of an inch in diameter. As we know, our eyes
normally can see a great deal. Suppose our eyes were
so immense that the pupils measured nearly *nine feet
across*, and that they also acted as huge magnifying
glasses! Then, like the 100-inch telescope, we could
see so far into space that we could detect light which

117

left stars millions of light years ago. These were the stars Dr. Hale wanted to see through this biggest of all glass eyes.

When darkness came they swung the 100-inch telescope toward the east, aimed at the planet Jupiter. Hale, trying to appear calm, yet failing to conceal his excitement, slowly brought his eye to the instrument. When he turned away a few moments later there was gloom in his tired face and his shoulders sagged as he stepped back to let Adams reach the eyepiece. Adams, too, was appalled by what he saw. Even the poet, Noyes, knew the reason when he glanced through the lens.

Instead of one bright image of Jupiter, there were five or six images, all overlapping each other, like a film with several double exposures of the same object.

The three men stood silently for a moment. Hale glanced at the opening in the dome. "Was the dome open today?" he asked. "Has the sun been shining on the mirror?"

They asked the watchman. Yes, he told them, the dome had been opened by workmen who were putting finishing touches on the mounting. If the sun had not hit the mirror directly, it had certainly shone on the covering above it. Perhaps the heat had temporarily distorted the glass.

For three hours they stayed in the dome, looking into the eyepiece occasionally. The overlapping images were still there.

They decided to go to their living quarters, but Hale and Adams evidently had no intention of sleeping. "We'll come back at three o'clock in the morning," they agreed. "Maybe the glass will have cooled down by then."

They were back soon after two-thirty. Jupiter was out of telescopic reach in the west. They pointed the instrument north to the bright star Vega. Hale, plainly distressed, approached the eyepiece. He glanced at Adams prayerfully, then peered through the lens. Almost immediately a wide grin brightened his thin face, and Adams knew that the 100-inch telescope was a success.

"In the morning," Adams wrote later, "we reported our experiences to Alfred Noyes. His instinct for the dramatic seized upon them and they have become a part of his great picture of the progress of astronomical science throughout the ages—*The Watchers of the Sky*."

In 1919 the 100-inch, 100-ton reflector was formally placed in operation at Mount Wilson. At the specific request of Andrew Carnegie, the $600,000 instrument was named the Hooker Telescope. It was used rarely for observing planets, satellites, asteroids or comets, because it was designed to explore "far-off, fainter things," such as the Milky Way and the universe beyond the Milky Way. By photography this telescope can "see" billions of stars. When we look at the stars with our unaided eyes, we see only about two thousand at any one time!

The Milky Way is made up of great clouds of gas, dust, and billions of stars. These constitute a *galaxy* in which our own solar system occupies a small place.

With the 100-inch telescope and spectroscopic equipment, the astronomers studied (and are still studying) temperatures, pressures, sizes, and masses of stars in the Milky Way. The huge telescope has helped them to determine that our solar system consists of one star (the sun), nine planets, thirty-odd satellites, several thousand asteroids, and more than one thousand comets. Our galaxy, which is a great whorl, or stellar system, contains more than one hundred billion stars, of which the sun is only one—and this galaxy is 100,000 light years in diameter.

What is a light-year? We know that light travels about 186,000 miles per second. Therefore, one light-year is the distance that light travels in one year—roughly six million million miles! And some galaxies are as far as one billion light years from the earth—perhaps farther. Even the light reflected by the moon takes one and one-fourth seconds to reach the earth. Light from the sun reaches us in eight minutes; from the nearest other star, four years; from the nearest galaxy, two million years, and from the farthest known galaxy, one billion years.

What Dr. Hale was seeking is best expressed in his own words, written in 1915 in a little book call *Ten Years' Work of a Mountain Observatory:*

"Let us suppose," he wrote, "as in the case of the Mount Wilson Observatory, that the chief object is to contribute in the highest degree possible to the solution of the problem of stellar evolution. What was the origin of this earth on which we live? We know that it is a member of a solar system, one of several planets moving harmoniously about a great central sun on which they depend for light and heat. But how was the earth formed? Through what successive stages did it pass in its early life? How were its constituent parts separated from that great vaporous mass which, as most astronomers believe, once united the planets and the sun? What is the nature of the central sun on which our lives depend? What is its relationship to other stars and what part does it play in the universe? How is this universe organized? What bodies does it comprise, what is its structure, and what are its bounds? If the processes of creation and evolution are still at work within it, may we not expect to find existing samples of the various stages through which our own solar system has passed?"

The 100-inch Hooker Telescope was making a significant stab into the reaches of outer space, thanks to the vision and enterprise of Dr. Hale. But the Hooker Telescope made Hale feel more than ever like the pioneer, the explorer who eagerly climbs a mountain to see what is on the other side, then finds a valley and beyond it another, higher, more rugged mountain. This, too, he must conquer.

In 1923, broken in health, Hale resigned as director of Mount Wilson. Unwilling to give up his work in astronomy, he built a small astronomical laboratory near his home. Though it was largely financed by Hale himself, both the Mount Wilson staff and the Carnegie Institution assisted him with the design and the equipment. Hale used the laboratory during his life, specifying that it was to be presented to the Carnegie Institution when he died.

As a part of his work, Hale wrote a number of

astronomical articles for the public. One of these, published in 1928, was entitled *The Possibilities of Large Telescopes*. In this article Hale suggested that although the Hooker Telescope was a magnificent instrument, it was reasonable to believe that reflecting telescopes could be made with mirrors 200 or even 300 inches in diameter.

This article was read with keen interest by members of three Rockefeller organizations—the General Education Board, the International Education Board, and the Rockefeller Foundation. After considerable discussion, the three offered to finance the building of what would be the most complete astronomical laboratory in the world, for the California Institute of Technology, on the basis of a plan whereby the Institute would cooperate with the Carnegie Institution and the Mount Wilson Observatory. Most important of all, the equipment for the laboratory was to include a reflecting telescope with a mirror 200 inches in diameter!

Here was a challenge to satisfy the most adventurous heart—a venture which would cost more than six million dollars, would take almost twenty years to complete, and which would enable man to span one billion, two hundred million light-years at a glance—provided, of course, that the mirror could be successfully produced. This was in some doubt, since nothing even approaching the manufacture of such a tremendous single reflector had ever been attempted.

Dr. Hale joined in the planning and early work,

but he died at the age of seventy in 1938, just ten years before his bold dream became a reality. "The Hale Telescope," however, makes his name a part of man's greatest astronomical marvel—the Mount Palomar Observatory and its 200-inch reflecting telescope.

CHAPTER NINE

THE SHINING GIANT

A "syrup" of more than twenty tons of molten glass was poured over a ceramic "waffle" seventeen feet in diameter to produce a disk for the biggest mirror the world has ever seen.

To understand the problems solved by the master technicians of the Corning Glass Works at Corning, New York, in making the disk for the 200-inch Mount Palomar reflector, we should know something about the manufacture of glass. The people at Corning have shared some of their knowledge with us and have revealed some surprising facts.

Glass, they say, is not really a solid, even though it may feel like one. It's made by melting and mixing together such substances as sand, lime and soda and permitting them to cool. In the cooling process the mixture does not crystallize, so instead of a solid it is actually a "supercooled liquid."

The first glass was made by nature on the slopes of volcanoes, where the terrific heat fused sand and other matter into a black transparent mass called *obsidian*. This natural glass was shaped by primitive man into arrowheads, knives, other weapons and tools, and later into jewelry and ornamental objects.

Man learned the secret of making glass hundreds

of years before Christ, and since that time he has invented ways of fashioning it into all sorts of useful objects—dishes, windows, bottles, light bulbs (in 1879 Corning made the bulb for Thomas Edison's first incandescent lamp), radio and television tubes, beads, spectacles, mirrors. Today, in fact, it is quite impossible for us to imagine a world without glass, yet the search for new kinds and new uses continues. The Corning Glass Works, founded in 1851, has more than 65,000 glassmaking formulas, but every week its experts melt and experiment with 200 new glass mixtures.

The many types of glass include lead glass, or crystal, soda-lime glass (for windows, bottles and other inexpensive items), colored glass (for traffic lights, sunglasses, filters), fiber glass (air filters, fishing rods, chairs)—and optical glass, used for lenses, mirrors, and other scientific apparatus.

Optical glass was not to be used for the 200-inch Palomar mirror, since the mirror was to be made for reflecting and photographing images—not as a transparent lens for visual observation. We might wonder why steel or some other metal was not used instead of glass. Remember the trouble Dr. Hale had when the warmth of the sun had distorted the glass in the 100-inch Hooker Telescope? Heat or cold would distort a 17-foot metal mirror so badly that it would be useless for telescopic work—and the scientists decided that the curvature of the Mount Palomar mirror must not be permitted to change more than *two millionths of an inch,* to be satisfactory.

This meant that a very special kind of glass would have to be used for the mirror, since many types of glass expand and contract in varying degrees with temperature changes.

In 1931 the Corning Glass Works was asked to try to make the great disk with glass like that called "Pyrex," which this company developed. Pyrex is the glass we find in the kitchens of many American homes today, used for casserole cooking, baking cakes and pies, and for other cookery. It is heat-resistant and has properties of expansion and contraction which are only one-third those of steel.

Nothing of the size of the Palomar mirror had ever before been fashioned of glass. The Corning experts, supervised by Dr. George V. McCauley, a physicist in the company's research laboratory, agreed to tackle the unique job.

Instead of making one huge solid disk, the experts agreed that the molten glass should be poured into a ribbed mold, which would give it great strength and minimum weight. If it were solid it would be so heavy (forty tons) that it would bend when the telescope was moved. The 114 ribs, or cores, were ceramic posts, both round and pie-shaped, standing about two thirds as high as the mold. Six of the pie-shaped posts circled each round piece, like petals around the center of a flower. All posts were anchored to the bottom of the mold with metal rods. When the mirror was finished, these cores would be removed, leaving the ribbed skeleton topped by a smooth glass surface of the desired thickness for the mirror.

Many tests were made before the company manufactured smaller (30-inch and 60-inch) mirrors, which would be used for testing and auxiliary purposes at Palomar, and which would also provide valuable experience for the men making the 200-incher. Climaxing the preliminary work was the making of a 120-inch mirror, which was then larger than any other, and which is now in use at Mount Hamilton. This task was successful, but these three mirrors were two years in the making, and the glass experts were not yet sure that they could produce the 200-inch mirror without imperfections.

The pouring of the great mirror began on March 25, 1934. This was a unique and complex operation. Pyrex could be melted only at terrific temperatures—about 2,700 degrees Fahrenheit—and the mirror must not cool quickly. For the earlier work Dr. McCauley had designed a dome-shaped oven which the workmen dubbed "the igloo." The huge mold was placed inside this oven, and gas burners heated the oven for ten days before the melting began. This was necessary so that the oven and mold would be hot enough to keep the glass in a liquid state until it filled all parts of the mold.

To pour the molten glass through three openings in the igloo, the workmen dipped it out of the melting tank with three heavy ladles, each having a twenty-foot handle, each ladle holding 400 pounds. Obviously the ladle would be too heavy for a man to carry alone, so each ladle was hung from an overhead trolley by a steel bar. Sweating and shouting, the workmen plunged the ladles into the molten sea and hauled them out. The glowing overflow splashed back into the tank as the great fiery dippers were rushed to the igloo and emptied into the waiting mold.

Suddenly disaster struck. The ceramic cores bobbed up to the surface of the mold. The metal anchor rods had been melted by the terrific heat. Dr. McCauley felt a terrible sinking sensation in the pit of his stomach. What to do? Should he stop the work abruptly? If he did, he would save a lot of labor. If he kept it going, he knew the glass would be useless for its intended purpose—but he might gain priceless knowledge from the experience. It was an agonizing moment. Finally he gave the order: Keep going!

The floating cores were broken into small pieces and the mold was filled. Next came the cooling operation, which was more ticklish than the casting. Too rapid cooling would crack the disk, or set up internal strains which would warp it. Since the disk itself was already useless for the mirror, Dr. McCauley speeded up the cooling process (called *annealing*) and carefully observed the disk at all its cooling stages, in preparation for the making of another. The first disk was placed on exhibition by the company and may still be seen at the Corning Glass Museum.

On December 2, 1934, they were ready to start the second 200-inch disk. This time the ceramic cores were anchored with special steel rods and were hollow, so that cool air could be sucked through the cores to keep the rods from melting in the oven.

The pouring took six hours. Dr. McCauley and the

others breathed deep sighs of relief when the mold was finally filled, but the delicate annealing operation lay ahead. The mold was placed in an electric annealing oven and kept there at an exact temperature for two months. For the next eight long anxious months the temperature was to be reduced by seven tenths of one degree (centigrade) each day. Then, with only three months to go, disaster threatened again.

Rivulets of water began to trickle into the Corning plant, and to grow into streams. The nearby Chemung River had flooded and was to rise higher than at any time in the previous seventeen years. The annealing oven was not directly in danger, but the electrical equipment used for heating was in the path of the flood. Practically everybody in the Corning plant— office workers, carpenters, electricians—pitched in to fill sandbags with almost anything and to build a barrier around the electrical life line. It was a losing battle. The water kept gaining. To protect the workers from possible electrocution, the current was turned off. The 200-inch disk was no longer under controlled heat. It might crack. It might warp. Anything might happen.

What did happen was that the current remained off for three days while McCauley and the others labored to get the electrical equipment to a higher location. Finally the power was restored, but no one knew whether the disk was ruined or not. And there was no way to be sure. It still had to cool for three months.

In October, 1935, when the cooling was almost

completed, the people of Corning were terrified when their homes shook, and dishes and other things fell to the floor. Earthquake! McCauley sped to the plant. If the quake had shaken the great disk . . . but it hadn't. The glass was apparently unharmed.

Soon afterwards it was removed from the oven—a great round platform of greenish glass, ready to be ground, polished, and shaped into a surface that would catch the light from stars which man did not yet know existed.

Shipping the mirror was a vexing problem. It was too wide to be laid flat on a railroad car, too high to pass under low bridges. A special car was ordered from the New York Central Railroad—a flat car with a long, wide slot in the floor so that the crate with the disk could be made secure, with its bottom close to the tracks. The crate was made of half-inch steel plates. Inside it, the disk was completely covered with thick rubber. Total weight: thirty-five tons.

As the crate waited to be moved from the Corning yards, once again the Chemung River went on a rampage. The water crept toward the disk. The yard grew muddy. Frantically the workmen jammed heavy planks into the muck to keep the truck-trailer from getting stuck when the crate was loaded.

Loading was still another problem. The water made it impossible to move in a crane to lift the disk to the trailer. Using heavy jacks, workmen raised the huge crate little by little—so slowly, in fact, that each movement was barely perceptible. One whole week went into the lifting and loading of the disk.

Across the rough plank road the trailer crawled, slowly, ever so slowly. The flood waters had left only a narrow strip of land for the roadway, and one side of the strip skirted the edge of the factory buildings. The loaded trailer reached the corner of one building, a corner that jutted out into its path. The water on the other side was still rising. There was only one thing to do. A crew of laborers hammered away the obstacle, demolishing part of the building—but it took another day to do it.

At a railroad siding in Corning, a giant crane used by the New York Central to lift locomotives was ready to pick up the steel crate and its precious contents. Within twenty-four hours the crate was gently lowered onto thick rubber pads in the slot in the railroad car, and was made secure. The following day it was to leave on its historic journey, but that was a day of disappointment. The crate had flattened the rubber pads and was almost touching the roadbed.

Another three or four weeks were lost in raising and repacking the disk. This time McCauley used gum rubber and blocks of wood, bolting the crate to the wood and placing heavy coil springs under the boltheads. Thick steel rods extended to the crate from the car corners. This time the load did not sag. The glass was ready for its cross-country journey.

The New York Central, the Burlington, and the Santa Fe Railroads worked together to get the shipment to California safely—a difficult feat requiring special rights-of-way, special routing to avoid hitting low bridges, and every precaution the railroaders could conceive, including night patrols of armed railroad policemen on sidings.

The shipment left Corning on March 26, 1936. When it arrived at Pasadena on the morning of April 10, it was discovered that its protective metal sheath was pockmarked with bullet dents, evidently from shots fired en route by farmers or hunters without harmful intent. The disk was safely delivered to the optical shops of the Mount Palomar Observatory at the California Institute of Technology in Pasadena. Now the real challenge was at hand. The rough glass had to be ground, polished and hollowed out to a true paraboloidal figure which must not vary more than two-millionths of an inch at any part of its 36,000 square inches.

The grinding was done with a complicated house-sized machine especially designed for the job. The turntable, or grinding "tool," was of steel, faced with blocks of the same kind of glass as the disk. The tool would cut by rubbing abrasives against the disk under pressure. The grinder was driven by several motors and a maze of gears, and could be made to move in any one of numerous patterns, a necessity if the disk were to be ground evenly.

At the start, to true up the rim, face, and back, some two and three-quarter tons of glass were ground off. Then the disk was placed in the mounting cell in which it would be fitted to the telescope. Cylindrical metal posts were inserted in the holes left by the round ceramic cores, and these posts held the disk securely in the cell.

132

Then came the job of grinding and polishing the disk to a precise paraboloidal surface. Steadily, for days, weeks, months—for more than eleven years (with interruptions because of World War II)—the grinding, polishing and shaping went on.

The man responsible for this nerve-racking task was a one-time truck driver named Marcus H. Brown, of Long Beach, California. Brown had worked on the construction of George Hale's private observatory, and later had driven trucks up and down Mount Wilson when the observatory was being built. Having only a sixth-grade education, and a deep interest in the optical business, he set up a home study program for himself in which he spent long hours at night studying optical theories and glass.

When the announcement was made about the proposed 200-inch telescope, Brown pleaded for a job in the laboratory and was hired as an apprentice. It was all he needed. He learned quickly, he conducted experiments of his own on mirrors, and soon he was skillful enough to make reflectors of his own—and good ones.

His continued studies, his construction of a satisfactory homemade grinding machine from spare automobile parts and from junk, his encouragement from his wife, and his eagerness to be among the best in his chosen line, won for Marcus Brown the distinction of supervising the completion of the world's greatest telescope mirror.

Though the work was interrupted by World War II, the task was finished on October 3, 1947. In all, more

133

than five tons of glass were ground from the disk by thirty-one tons of abrasives, ranging from coarse to very fine. The finished disk was about 24 inches thick at the rim and 20¼ inches at the center, which is exactly 3¾ inches below the rim. From its original weight of twenty tons it was reduced to fourteen and one-half tons.

In 1947 the disk was moved to the observatory at Mount Palomar, where it was coated with a brilliant aluminum film and subjected to tests and adjustments for about another year. Finally it was installed in the 60-foot, 150-ton telescope, giving the instrument a total weight of about one million pounds. Yet it is so delicately balanced that it is moved easily with an electric motor of one-twelfth horsepower.

This massive telescope stands under a dome which is some twelve stories high and just about as wide (137 feet). Like some skeletal skyscraper, the telescope pivots between the arms of a U-shaped mounting. The "U" is fixed in a tipped position at an angle of about 45 degrees. Its two arms are fastened at right angles to a horseshoe-shaped bearing which is cradled in a massive pier, curved to fit the bearing. Thus the huge instrument may be swung up or down on its pivot, and to right or left by the horseshoe.

Strangely enough, this optical marvel is not intended to be looked through. It is used for making photographs or analyzing the light of celestial bodies —mostly stars and galaxies which cannot be "seen" by any other instrument. From these observations astronomers are today trying to determine such things as how big the universe is and whether it is changing in size; how stars and planetary systems are born, grow, and die; and whether, as seems probable, nuclear energy gives the stars their tremendous power. When the "image multiplier" is perfected, as mentioned in Chapter 6, it will make the 200-inch mirror equivalent to one measuring 2,000 inches! Instead of its present range of 12,000 billion billion miles, this telescope may be able to "see" 36 billion trillion miles into space!

Valued teammate of the 200-inch telescope is a 48-inch Schmidt (camera) telescope, which is unsurpassed for some purposes. In 1956 this telescope took the last of 1,758 celestial photographs to complete an atlas of the sky. This project, sponsored jointly by the National Geographic Society and Mount Palomar Observatory, has produced what scientists appropriately call "a portrait of the universe," which is now under study by many observatories and other scientific institutions.

On June 3, 1948, the 200-inch reflector was dedicated at Mount Palomar in the presence of hundreds of leading scientists and educators. There it was officially christened "The Hale Telescope," in honor of Dr. George Ellery Hale.

Today the Mount Wilson and Mount Palomar Observatories are operated jointly by the Carnegie Institution of Washington and the California Institute of Technology. The business address of both observatories is the same—813 Santa Barbara Street, Pasadena 4, California. At Mount Wilson the observatory grounds are always open. The visitors' gallery at the 100-inch Hooker telescope is open from 1:30 to 4:30 P.M. Monday through Friday, and from 11:00 A.M. to 4:30 P.M. on Saturdays and Sundays. No tickets are required, no charge is made by the observatory—but a fee is collected by the Mount Wilson Hotel Company, which owns the property on which the observatory is located.

At Mount Palomar visitors are permitted to see the 200-inch telescope from a gallery in the dome, and an astronomical museum, any day in the week from 9:30 A.M. to 4:30 P.M. without charge. They are not, however, permitted to enter the room where the Hale telescope stands, because the mirror is so sensitive to heat and cold.

Only at the time of the 1948 dedication ceremonies were visitors permitted to have a close look at the gleaming mirror which, in its gigantic setting, makes every onlooker feel truly insignificant. In the ceremonies, Dr. Raymond B. Fosdick, then president of the Rockefeller Foundation, which financed the $6,550,000 observatory, included this remark: "Adrift in a cosmos whose shores he cannot even imagine, man spends his energies in fighting with his fellow man over issues which a single look through this telescope would show to be utterly inconsequential."

Although F. G. Pease of the Mount Wilson staff made preliminary designs of the Mount Palomar installation, it remained for an artist, an architect, a Polar explorer, and a musician to contribute artistic drawings of the telescope-to-be, drawings which were invaluable in the completion of the telescope. These professions were wrapped up in one individual named Russell W. Porter, whose magnificent drawings of the 200-inch reflector appear today in textbooks and encyclopedias dealing with it. But Russell Porter's greatest contribution to astronomy was in terms of people rather than art or architecture.

Every year thousands of people visit Mount Wilson, Mount Palomar, Lick, Yerkes, and all the other great and small astronomical observatories in the United States. Many are simply curious, but thousands have a deep and serious interest in telescopes and astronomy. These are the men, women and children who can be found across our country and around the world— the so-called "amateur astronomers" whose knowledge of telescopes and of the heavens often penetrates well into the "professional" class. Russell Porter devoted much of his life to arousing in these men and women a genuine interest in astronomy, showing them how they could make new friends, learn new and fascinating things about the stars and planets—and with it all, how they could have a lot of clean and profitable fun.

CHAPTER TEN

ENJOY THE TELESCOPE YOU HAVE

Russell Porter didn't start out to be an amateur astronomer or a telescope maker. Born December 13, 1871, in Springfield, Vermont, he studied architecture at the Massachusetts Institute of Technology. While a student he attended a lecture by Admiral Robert E. Peary, the Polar explorer, whose yarns about the Arctic sparked an urge in Porter to see the north for himself.

Between 1894 and 1906, Porter made twelve exploration trips to the Polar regions with Peary and also with Cook and Ziegler. His last trip was almost his last earthly act. The Ziegler expedition was shipwrecked on Franz Josef Land, where Porter and his companions suffered and starved for some two and one-half years before they were rescued.

After months of rest and convalescence, Porter began to design and build houses. In 1911 he happened to read a magazine article by a man who had made a telescope. Porter tried his own hand at making a 2-inch reflector, which was successful, and from that time forward his eyes were on the stars.

During World War I he worked in the optical section of the Bureau of Standards in Washington. In 1921 he wrote his first article about amateur telescope-making (published in *Popular Astronomy*, a magazine no longer in existence). The article was read by Albert G. Ingalls, then editor of *Scientific American*, who was later to play a significant part in Porter's life.

Returning to his Springfield home after World War I, Porter worked as an optician for James Hartness, of the Jones and Lamson Machine Company, who was also an amateur astronomer. The two became close personal friends. Porter made some fifty 6-inch reflectors for others, and his enthusiastic interest in astronomy was so contagious that his fellow workers were soon building telescopes of their own. They pooled their resources and built an observatory on the outskirts of town—an observatory they called *Stellafane*, which is today a Mecca for amateur astronomers.

Word of Porter's stargazers soon reached Albert Ingalls, who went to Springfield and commissioned Porter to write several articles for the *Scientific American* on how to build telescopes. Ingalls also publicized Porter in the magazine, so that news about Stellafane flashed like a comet, and hundreds of amateur astronomers began to write to Porter and gradually to visit him and his associates at Springfield.

When George Hale sought an artist to help with the projected 200-inch Mount Palomar reflector, it was

Albert Ingalls who introduced Hale to Russell Porter, and soon afterwards Porter was invited to go to California to work on the huge telescope. His remarkable drawings of it have become famous. He left Vermont in 1928 and until he died on February 22, 1949, he worked at Palomar and at the California Institute of Technology in Pasadena. In all that time he never failed to encourage the amateur astronomer, whose contributions to the science of astronomy are today more valuable than ever.

If you have an astronomical telescope and don't already belong to an amateur astronomical organization, local or national, you ought to join one, not only to make new friends and to swap ideas, but also to get help and advice if you need it, and to keep posted on developments in your particular specialty.

If you have no specialty you should consider choosing one and becoming an authority on it. The professional astronomer must spend years making an intensive study of the science as a whole, but the serious amateur may select one phase in which to concentrate his work, and perhaps become more of an expert in his field than many professionals. In any case, use your telescope time to good advantage. Don't make a random observation now and then just for the fun of it, when you can just as easily make systematic and useful observations and report your results to professional astronomers who need your help because they don't have the time for such work.

Most amateurs specialize in one of several fields: variable stars; comet hunting; sunspot counting;

meteors; occultation (concealment) of stars by the moon; observations of the zodiacal light; observations of lunar and planetary markings (some parts of the moon have not yet been completely charted).

Perhaps the most important of these is the observation of variable stars. A variable star is one whose brightness increases and decreases. Here is a mystery which astronomers are still trying to solve, and which offers great investigative opportunities for the amateur. Science has to know exactly how these stars pulsate before looking into the reasons for the fluctuations. Only by thousands of careful observations can the answer to the first question be found—and it is primarily a job for the amateur, because the huge telescopes in the observatories are devoted to other important tasks in other celestial fields.

To learn how to go about making observations of variable stars, write to the nation's oldest amateur astronomical group, the American Association of Variable Star Observers (AAVSO) in care of Mrs. Margaret W. Mayall, Recording Secretary, 4 Brattle Street, Cambridge 38, Massachusetts.

Are you interested in counting sunspots? Frequently the daytime skies are overcast in the regions of the big observatories, making solar observation impossible. At the same time, however, amateur sunspot counters in other locations may have a clear view of the sun and an opportunity to observe sunspots of brief duration (some last only a few hours) which the professionals would otherwise never know about. The AAVSO has a Solar Division specializing in sunspot observations. Caution: Never look directly at the sun with (or without!) your telescope. Protect your eyes with a dark glass or filter. Better yet, let your telescope project the sun's image on a paper or sunscreen mounted behind the eyepiece.

If you are a calm and patient person with a yen for hunting, then hunting for comets might be your wise choice. You need patience because you might scan the skies for months and months without finding a comet. You will use charts showing known stellar bodies which merely look like comets. There will be exciting moments when you're sure you've discovered a new comet—and then you'll examine your charts and learn that it's only a little old nebula which everyone knows about. But . . . .

There will be other heart-pounding times when you can't find your discovery on your chart. You'll watch it for perhaps a couple of hours to trace its movement—and suddenly you'll know you're a successful hunter. It's a new comet! You'll send a wire to Harvard Observatory and when your find is confirmed, Harvard will announce it to the astronomical world. You may even have it named for you and win fame and a medal, as Maria Mitchell did many years ago.

Maria Mitchell, born August 1, 1818, in Nantucket, Massachusetts, was the daughter of a Quaker whaling captain who was also an enthusiastic astronomer. With his telescope he showed Maria the moon, stars and planets, in which she became deeply interested. She also had a love for mathematics, and eventually became so expert at figures that she could solve complex problems which even stumped her Nantucket schoolteachers.

While still a young girl Maria was offered a job as town librarian, which gave her a marvelous opportunity to read scores of books on science and astronomy. After dark, however, most of her time was spent at her telescope, and she began to take a special interest in comets, locating several and working out their orbits by mathematical calculations. On October 1, 1847, she was thrilled to discover what she believed to be a new comet—one that no other human had yet detected. With her father she reported her find to astronomers in Boston, who promptly relayed the news to Europe, astronomical center of the world at that time. Maria anxiously awaited confirmation of her discovery, and when it finally came it was accompanied by professional recognition which changed her whole life. The comet was named for her, she was awarded a medal by the King of Denmark, elected to membership in the American Academy of Arts and Sciences and other scientific societies, and was presented with a fine astronomical telescope by a group of American women.

In 1861, Maria became interested in plans being made by Matthew Vassar for a new institution to be known as Vassar Female College (later Vassar College). This now-famous institution opened in 1865 with Maria Mitchell as its first Professor of Astronomy, a post in which she served with distinction until her retirement in 1888. She died at Lynn, Massachusetts, on June 28, 1889, at the age of seventy-one.

Modern comet-hunters, following in Maria Mitchell's skysteps, are constantly at work all over the world. On October 18, 1957, for example, 32-year-old Paul Wild of Bern, Switzerland, once a student at Mount Palomar Observatory, reported his discovery of a new comet to the Astronomical Institute of Bern University. Astronomers verified his find, estimating that the comet was about 6,210,000 miles from the earth, and moving in a southeasterly direction. Named for its young discoverer, the short-tailed visitor was officially recorded as the "Wild Comet."

If you have a quick eye and can get away from city lights and city haze, you'd be ideal for observing meteors. For this contribution to science you don't need a telescope. Astronomers and space scientists are more interested in meteors than ever before, and the more information they can accumulate about them, the more they will know about planning for outer space travel. The American Meteor Society is composed of professional and amateur astronomers interested in the study of meteors. Membership lists were closed in 1957 because the Society had more applications than it could handle effectively, but you can obtain information about its work by writing to Mr. Charles P. Olivier, 521 North Wynnewood Avenue, Narberth, Pennsylvania.

Perhaps you would like to play a game of heavenly hide-and-seek. Then star occultations by the moon are for you and your telescope. When the moon passes between the earth and a star or planet, hiding it from our sight, we call this an occultation. Because the moon is so bright, however, a telescope must be used to establish the exact moments of the star's disappearance and reappearance. Astronomers say they need thousands of these observations to make a more exact determination of the moon's path, to identify changes in the earth's rate of rotation, and to establish other important facts.

The observatories would like more information about the zodiacal light. This is a mysterious half-oval-shaped glow, often seen above the horizon just after sunset or just before sunrise, mostly in tropical zones or from high mountains. Scientists are not yet sure what causes it, or whether it is in or beyond the earth's atmosphere. The more information they can get about the dates it is observed, its duration, approximate height and shape, the better able they will be to learn its secret. A telescope isn't necessary for this kind of observation, but would make it more interesting.

Studies of the moon and planets are of great value, because the appearance of the planets changes constantly, and scientists want to be aware of each change and to find the reasons for it. Here again there is an organization of amateurs specializing in this field. It is the Association of Lunar and Planetary Observers (ALPO), and its members are grouped in units according to their special interests—Mars, Jupiter, Saturn, Venus, Mercury, the moon. Their findings are reported in the Association's monthly journal, *The*

Strolling Astronomer. For more information, write to Mr. Walter H. Haas, Director, 1203 North Alameda Boulevard, Las Cruces, New Mexico.

By far the largest national organization of amateur astronomers is The Astronomical League, whose member clubs hold annual and regional conventions at which the amateurs talk shop and exchange useful ideas. Members of the League receive subscriptions to *Sky and Telescope,* probably the most popular magazine for amateur astronomers, published by the Sky Publishing Corporation, Harvard College Observatory, Cambridge 38, Massachusetts.

The Astronomical League is made up of about 140 local amateur astronomical clubs or groups, totaling some 7,000 individuals. If you want to belong to such a club, but if there is none in your area, you may still become a member of the League and attend its annual or regional meetings. Both the AAVSO and ALPO are affiliate members of the League. Many commercial firms, including telescope manufacturers and local business houses, hold "supporting memberships" in the League.

For more information about the League and its activities, write to its Executive Secretary, Mrs. Wilma Cherup, 4 Klopfer Street, Pittsburgh 9, Pennsylvania.

There is another amateur organization, the Western Astronomers Association, which is similar to the Astronomical League and which centers its activity in the West. For information about this federation write to Mr. Walter Marion, 3516 Lyon Avenue, Oakland, California.

In Canada, the Royal Astronomical Society of Canada is glad to lend a helping hand to amateur astronomers, and publishes *The Observers' Handbook*, which is of value to every stargazer. National Secretary of the Society is Mr. E. J. A. Kennedy, 252 College Street, Toronto, Ontario, Canada.

There are many local organizations which are not members of the national bodies, but which would be happy to help would-be astronomers get started on telescopes and observations. You can probably learn from your Public Library whether or not such a group exists in your community. If the library doesn't know, write to the nearest observatory or to *Sky and Telescope* magazine, which undoubtedly can furnish the address of an amateur group near you.

If you have a telescope and if there isn't any amateur organization in your area, why not start one yourself? Get others interested in your instrument and work and encourage them to make or buy telescopes of their own. The Astronomical League will be glad to send you printed material to help you organize and maintain an amateur group.

Telescopes and binoculars are also valuable for studying and identifying land and sea birds, and many ornithologists as well as amateur bird-watchers use these instruments for their work or their hobby, as the case may be.

Rifle and pistol shooters also use telescopes, or "spotting scopes," to get a close-up view of the targets at which they shoot, both in practice and in contests. Mostly, however, the telescope today is used for studying the stars, or for tracking rockets, missiles, or artificial satellites.

The hero of a modern success story about amateur astronomers is named Clyde Tombaugh. In 1928, when he was about twenty-two, Tombaugh lived on a Kansas wheat farm. For several years, as a hobby, he had made observations with telescopes of his own manufacture, specializing in Mars. He made numerous drawings of the so-called "canals" and finally sent the drawings to Lowell Observatory at Flagstaff, Arizona.

The director, Dr. E. C. Slipher, noted for his own studies of Mars, was so impressed that he invited Tombaugh to the observatory. After some discussions, Dr. Slipher offered him a job—searching for a planet which might or might not exist, a planet which the late Dr. Percival Lowell had once predicted would be found in a certain area.

For a year Tombaugh searched the region where the planet might be. It was filled with thousands of stars, yet in the faintest part of the heavenly display he found his planet. His findings were checked for another year, to be sure he was right. He was. The planet we now call Pluto, one of the smallest of those we know.

Clyde Tombaugh's discovery won him a scholarship at the University of Kansas, and later an important role in Uncle Sam's top-secret rocket program. As this is written, he is the only living human who has discovered a new planet—and it all began with a home-made telescope on a Kansas farm.

Many communities have been pleasantly surprised to learn that young people take a deep interest in astronomy. One of the most unique groups in the country is the Junior Astronomy Club of the Children's Museum, 1501 Montgomery Street, Fort Worth 7, Texas. This club, for elementary and high school students and for adult beginners, was organized by an unusual woman with an unusual name—Miss Charlie M. Noble. Explaining her name, Charlie Noble says, "My parents wanted a boy—but I was their only child!"

Miss Noble, who formerly headed the Department of Mathematics at Paschal Senior High School, began to teach classes in astronomy at the Children's Museum about 1947, but needed small telescopes. She bought a "Skyscope" and let her youthful members take turns using it. More and more young people became interested and joined her class, so the need for more telescopes grew accordingly. One or two more were purchased with members' dues or as gifts from citizens, but more had to be obtained. How could the money be raised?

It occurred to Miss Noble that if people paid small sums to borrow books from a rental library, perhaps they would also pay for the rental of telescopes. Instead of furnishing the instruments free to the increasing numbers of boys and girls coming to her classes, she began to charge a small fee for renting the telescopes. Usually one was rented by three or four students in a group, so that the cost per student was negligible. All of the rental money was reinvested in more telescopes, and the popularity of Miss Noble's classes is still growing. She also teaches her students how to make their own telescopes.

A living testimonial to Charlie Noble is seventeen-year-old Kay Gross, president of the Fort Worth Children's Museum Senior Astronomy Club. In her own words, here are some of Kay's accomplishments:

"I have made about six thousand observations of constellations, stars, planets, sun and moon, nebulae, double stars, galaxies, the Milky Way and globular clusters. I joined the club when I was ten years old. My telescopic observations are made with a 3½-inch Skyscope reflector, which I won by placing first in a competitive examination. My first telescope, which I bought, I then gave to the boy who placed second."

Kay Gross, like others, found that astronomy made closer family ties. "My family and I," she says, "have visited five planetariums and fifteen observatories all over the United States. I have met and corresponded with famous astronomers and have made lifelong friends through the study of astronomy. I've represented the Astronomy Club in two national conventions of the Astronomical League. I have won 138 'stars' (awards by the Club) for observing, reading, giving talks to school groups, visiting observatories, and winning the telescope."

Miss Noble awards a "Junior Astronomer" pin to each student who passes an examination given by her. The exam is no cinch. Here are just a few things the Junior Astronomer must do to qualify for the award:

Read and be able to give a brief report on at least five books on astronomy at his reading level.

Know twenty constellations; make records of observations; give time, date, and location of each observation.

Know and be able to locate at least fifteen stars of first magnitude.

Chart positions of Jupiter, Mars and Saturn over a period of four weeks or more. Indicate with an arrow the direction of each.

Draw a diagram showing relation of sun, moon and earth at new moon; first quarter; full moon; and last quarter.

Draw a diagram showing relation of sun, moon and earth at an eclipse of the sun, and another for eclipse of the moon.

Submit a logbook containing a record of all observational work, showing whether observations were made with naked eye or an optical aid, and show type of optical aid; show date, time, location, weather, temperature, seeing conditions, subject, results.

A major attraction of the Children's Museum in Fort Worth is the Charlie M. Noble Planetarium, named in honor of Miss Noble, the gift of Mr. and Mrs. Kenneth W. Davis of Forth Worth. It was made by Spitz Laboratories, headed by Mr. Armand N. Spitz, whose skill has enabled us to bring the entire heavens into our living and schoolrooms at a reasonable cost.

What is a planetarium? Says Mr. Spitz, "A planetarium is a projector, a combination of optical, mechanical and electrical equipment, to form a kind of time and space machine. It shows the stars on a man-made sky while the sun shines outdoors or while clouds form an overhead blanket. In a few seconds it carries audiences through hours, days, months, years, and centuries. It re-creates the sights of nature, has revolutionized the teaching of astronomy, and has had extraordinary influence in many other ways."

The first planetarium was made by the Carl Zeiss Optical Company in Germany in 1923. Originally the planetarium consisted of a complicated device shaped like a huge dumbbell, so costly that its installation was a rarity. Big planetariums in the United States are comparatively few—located in New York, Chicago, Pittsburgh, Philadelphia, Chapel Hill (N.C.), San Francisco and Los Angeles. Others are being installed in Boston, Flint (Mich.), and the Air Force Academy at Colorado Springs.

Today, thanks to Armand Spitz, the amateur astronomer can carry a small globular planetarium to his living room, dining room, porch or basement without difficulty, and with this scientific toy can see the stars on his ceiling just as though he were out of doors on a clear night. Spitz also makes more elaborate planetariums, including a model which has been accepted as the standard astronomical training device of the United States Navy, Air Force, Army, and Coast Guard.

The serious amateur astronomer can learn a great deal from a planetarium study of the stars. For information about various models and prices of Spitz

Planetariums you may write to the Spitz Laboratories, Inc., Yorklyn, Delaware.

Armand Spitz, incidentally, is the Coordinator of Visual Observations for "Operation Moonwatch," the project in which amateur astronomers were asked to use telescopes to track the artificial satellite to be launched by the United States during the International Geophysical Year.

The age of artificial satellites, guided missiles, and spaceships is upon us, and the use of telescopes for making observations in these fields is growing in importance. If you don't have a telescope of your own, why not get one? Here's how . . .

CHAPTER ELEVEN

GET YOURSELF
A TELESCOPE

You can make a simple refracting telescope quite easily and inexpensively. It won't be of professional caliber and it won't bring the stars within touching distance, but with it you might be able to see the larger valleys and mountains on the moon and enough other celestial sights to make you want to spend more time at stargazing.

You will need two lenses and two tubes. For the larger lens, or objective, you may use a lens from a pair of spectacles of the type sold in dime stores (I paid one dollar for a pair). Regular "curve-corrected" spectacle lenses are not suitable for telescope-making.

For the smaller lens, or eyepiece, I used a small, cheap magnifying glass which had been put away in a bureau drawer.

By lining up the smaller lens behind the larger lens (just as old Jan Lippershey's little boy did centuries ago), and looking at a distant object until it was clear, I determined how long a tube I would need to hold the lenses. It happened that mine was small—less than a foot long. Depending upon the kind of lens you use for your objective, you might need a tube three or four feet long, perhaps longer.

For lack of any better material to make the tubes, I rolled up pieces of thin cardboard which the laundry had used to return my laundered shirts. I rolled one piece tightly around the objective (which was about half an inch from the tube end) and the other I rolled so that it was just a bit smaller than the first and could slide in and out quite easily. I put pieces of gummed paper around the tubes to keep them round.

I had to fit the eyepiece into a cardboard "plug" at the end of its tube, because the eyepiece was smaller than the open end of the tube.

By moving the eyepiece tube back and forth, I could bring objects into focus at various distances. They were all upside down, but this is of little importance in observing the moon and stars. I covered both tubes with ordinary aluminum foil, merely to hide the rough cardboard and gummed paper! It is also a good idea to darken the inside of the tube with black ink or nonglossy paint, to absorb stray light (See Figure 10).

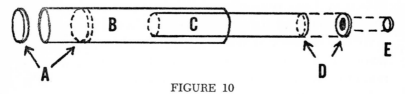

FIGURE 10

THE NEAL ONE-BUCK TELESCOPE

Convex spectacle (objective) lens A (from dime store) is rolled tightly into end of cardboard tube B, which is held rolled with gummed paper (or Scotch tape). Smaller cardboard tube C is rolled to fit snugly into tube B. Cardboard "plug" D is cut to fit into eyepiece end, and has hole in the center to accommodate small magnifying glass E, which is the eyepiece. Sliding tube C back and forth brings objects into focus. Length of tubes varies with focal length of objective lens.

155

My sixteen-year-old son suggested improvising a mounting by using my camera tripod. We took a small scrap of white pine and drilled a hole just a little smaller than the diameter of the threaded bolt which would ordinarily hold the camera to the tripod. Then we used strips of half-inch adhesive tape to hold the wood block to the telescope tube. Finally we screwed the assembly down on the camera holder and our mounting was complete. Not an equatorial or Warner and Swasey mounting, but at least it held the instrument steadier than our hands could.

With a very rough and simple instrument such as this you can get only a taste of the fun you might have with a bigger and better telescope. Many amateurs grind, polish and figure their own lenses and mirrors, but whole books have been written on this subject alone, and there is not enough space in this book to include detailed lessons on the subject. You should be aware, though, that the grinding and polishing of lenses and mirrors is hard and tedious work, requiring patience, time and elbow grease. The rewards are worth-while, but there are also other ways to proceed.

At the outset you will want to decide whether you want a reflector or a refractor. Both are efficient. The reflector will cost less money in the beginning, but it will eventually require servicing—principally resilvering of the mirror when it tarnishes. If you decide to build your own telescope, a reflector will be easier and cheaper to make than a refractor, although amateur astronomers make and use both types.

Most amateur astronomical groups or clubs conduct telescope-making classes for their members. By joining such a club you can receive competent instruction in the making of a telescope which, when completed, should be of good quality. You will also be taught how to use it, and you will have pleasant evenings together with other members having similar interests.

If you cannot join a local group and want to make your own telescope, you may buy glass disks, abrasives, tools, and other do-it-yourself supplies from numerous dealers in telescopes and telescope-making materials, all with the necessary instructions.

If you do not want to attempt to grind and polish your own lenses or mirrors, you may buy finished lenses and mirrors of various sizes, as well as telescopes, tubes, mountings—even professional observatory buildings, complete with domes—from commercial manufacturers specializing in these fields.

Obviously we cannot reproduce entire catalogues here, and we cannot recommend any firm as being better than others in the same business. In fairness, we have listed the names and addresses of numerous concerns in the back of the book, and any of them will be glad to send you printed catalogues and price lists upon request. However, to give you some idea of the kind of equipment you may buy, and its cost, we have selected some catalogue items from a few of these firms.

The Edmund Scientific Company, Barrington, New Jersey, sells telescopes and accessories, tools, binoculars, microscopes, photographic equipment, lenses, prisms and many other optical products. It makes and sells (for $49.50) the "Edscorp Satellite Telescope," especially for use in "Operation Moonwatch," tracking the artificial satellite. It offers a "Moonscope," a 3-inch reflecting telescope made by the makers of Spitz Planetariums, for $14.95. Other telescopes, both reflectors and refractors, range in price from $29.50 to $295. For beginners there are lenses for objectives costing from $2.50 up, and for eyepieces as low as $1.50. There is a complete kit, including finished mirror and eyepiece lens for a 3-inch reflecting telescope, for $10.95. All kits come with assembly instructions.

Another company, the Unitron Instrument Division of the United Scientific Company, 204-6 Milk Street, Boston 9, Massachusetts, publishes a catalogue with illustrations of more expensive telescopes, showing a price range from $75 for a 1.6-inch refractor, complete with mounting, to $1,280 for a 4-inch "photo-equatorial with fixed pier, clock drive, and astro-camera." Unitron also offers telescope accessories—lenses, eyepieces, mountings, clock drives, and viewfinders. The Unitron catalogue contains considerable interesting information about astronomical observing, choosing telescopes, and pointers for amateur astronomers.

The Criterion Manufacturing Company, 331 Church Street, Hartford 1, Connecticut, sells telescope accessories, kits, lenses, mirrors, eyepieces, mountings, and completed telescopes. One specialty for hobbyists, amateurs, students and Boy Scouts, is a 3-foot telescope, complete with star map, carrying case, and tripod, selling for $11.95. It will, says the catalogue, "bring distant objects, people, moon, stars, ships, etc., 105 times closer." Latest specialty of this company is a 4-inch reflecting telescope, the "Dynascope," costing $44.95 f.o.b. Hartford.

Criterion also sells a small "Spitz Jr. Planetarium" (14 inches high on a 7-by-7-inch base) for $14.95 postpaid. This is the "scientific toy" mentioned in Chapter 10. A helpful 126-page booklet, *Discover the Stars,* by Gaylord Johnson (with additions by John J. Krewalk of the Criterion Company), is included in the cost of some purchases from this firm.

Harry Ross, 61 Reade Street, New York 7, N. Y., deals in telescopes, microscopes, and other scientific apparatus. His catalogue includes a 3-inch "Ross Stellarscope," a Newtonian reflector which comes "ready to assemble in 15 minutes" at a cost of $16.50. Tripod and mounting equipment is extra. A 5-inch mirror for those who want to build their own reflectors can be bought here for $17. Other accessories are described in literature which Mr. Ross will send upon request.

The Cave Optical Company, 4137 East Anaheim Street, Long Beach 4, California, specializes in reflectors, "the poor man's telescope." Lowest priced instrument in its catalogue is a 6-inch reflector (26 inches long, described as "portable"), for $125, f.o.b. Long Beach. Others, with mirrors as large as 16 inches, range upward to $3,500.

Another Long Beach firm, Coast Instrument, Inc., 4811 Long Beach Boulevard, Long Beach 5, California, also produces a "Moonwatch" telescope made to Government specifications—cost, $49.50. This firm makes reflectors and refractors, binoculars, microscopes, and deals in "amateur telescope makers' supplies." Its catalogue specialty is the "Treckerscope," a reflecting telescope with mirrors ranging in diameter from 6 to 12½ inches. Price ranges are from $295 to $1150 f.o.b. Long Beach.

Mr. Oliver Floyd of this firm has a word of advice. "Too many uninitiated amateurs are 'power happy'," he says. "They should be made to realize that power is not everything in viewing. Often a better image is received by using lower powers. Most of the extremely large reflectors, such as those at Mount Palomar and Mount Wilson, normally employ very low powers in connection with their huge instruments—mostly way under 100 power."

Mr. Floyd has one other comment about the advantages of belonging to amateur astronomical groups. "These groups," he says, "often have star parties which are quite entertaining, and which have been known to lead to romantic tie-ups between boys and girls." Moonlight and starglow, in other words, may become occupational hazards—or delights—for many a romantic amateur!

In Springfield, Vermont, home of "Stellafane," Mr. John M. Pierce of Highland Road, has been a telescope maker for thirty years. He sells plain glass or Pyrex kits for telescope mirrors, at prices from $5 to $50, including everything you'll need to grind and polish your own mirror. Mr. Pierce specializes in materials for amateur telescope makers.

The famous firm of J. W. Fecker, Inc., mentioned earlier, in 1957 made available to the amateur a fine telescope—a 4-inch reflector, fully equipped, with a very steady equatorial mount and an electric sidereal drive, costing less than $200.

These are a representative few of the companies from which you may buy raw materials, kits for assembly, or finished telescopes. The prices shown are subject to change, but were in effect at the time of writing (1957).

Before investing any significant sum of money in a telescope for your own use, it will be wise for you to study some books about telescopes and astronomy (see Bibliography), to help you decide whether or not your investment is warranted. If there is an amateur astronomical group in your area, arrange to look through a telescope of one of its members, and to talk with several about stargazing in general. If it has enough appeal, then consider making or buying your telescope.

You may discover, however, that it isn't as fascinating as you thought. In that case it would be a waste of money for you to buy a telescope, since you probably wouldn't use it once the novelty wore off. On the other hand, if and when you do look through a good astronomical telescope for the first time, you may be so intrigued by the celestial show that you can't wait to get or make an instrument of your very own.

Many amateurs make telescopes which are professional in every sense of the word. In Washington, D. C., a twenty-year-old college student has a backyard observatory which houses a magnificent 8-inch

Newtonian reflector, complete with mounting, tracking device, guide telescope (finder), and astronomical photographic equipment. Philip Lichtman, son of a prominent Washington physician, not only constructed the observatory building, but also made the telescope and its mounting and accessories—except for the mirrors and lenses, which were bought in finished form.

The observatory's shining dome was fashioned from aluminum strips originally designed for a farm silo. The portion on which the dome rests is brick, and the inside walls are pine-paneled. The dome is not motor-driven, but is rotated by manpower, riding on ball-bearing roller-skate wheels. The building is about fourteen feet high.

All parts of the telescope and mounting were actually made by young Lichtman in his do-it-yourself machine shop in the basement of his home, and some features are of his own design. Construction of the telescope, the mounting, and the observatory took about two years (one year for the mounting alone).

Philip Lichtman, majoring in astronomy at Harvard University, says he cannot remember what first made him interested in telescopes and the stars. It began when he was about thirteen years old, and in the seven years since that time he has made three complete telescopes and telescope mountings.

"I do it just for fun," he says. "And I'm interested primarily in photographing the skies, rather than observing visually."

Some of his astronomical photographs, made with

regular commercial equipment, rank in quality with those of the larger observatories. He develops and prints his own pictures, which include excellent views of Mars, Jupiter, Saturn, nebulae, and several unusual close-ups of the craters of the moon.

Philip is a member of the National Capital Astronomers Club, a Washington amateur group with some 200 members. Occasionally he makes drawings showing his observations. One night when the "seeing" was particularly good, he invited a group of children to visit the observatory and look at the planet Saturn. The youngsters ranged in age from five to twelve years. He asked each of them to look carefully at the planet, then to draw a picture of what they saw. Even one of the five-year-olds produced a recognizable "portrait" of the planet, mysterious rings and all.

Philip Lichtman's telescope and observatory undoubtedly cost more than the average amateur could afford, but they demonstrate the extent to which the young stargazer can explore this scientific hobby—and the amateur who grinds and polishes a four-inch mirror of his own may get even more enjoyment from it than Mr. Lichtman and others who buy theirs readymade.

Today there are opportunities for youth in another kind of modern astronomy, a growing field involving a twentieth century invention for exploring the skies electronically—the radio telescope.

CHAPTER TWELVE

DOWN HERE...
AND OUT THERE

Man has not yet been able to touch any planet except Earth. With the optical telescope, however, he can *see* the planets, stars, sun and moon in magnified form. Now, with the radio telescope, he can also *hear* them.

No, they don't send messages, á la Western Union. They do send toward the earth what scientists call "electromagnetic energy waves," or radio waves. Although the celestial bodies are continually shooting these radiations toward the earth, there is a barrier in space which interferes with the signals. This is the ionosphere—the blanket which keeps our earthly radio broadcasts from floating away in space by bouncing our man-made radio waves back to earth and into our receivers.

The optical telescope can see through this invisible barrier. By using a short-wave-length radio range, the radio astronomer has also been able to find a hole in the ionosphere blanket and has made some interesting discoveries.

For example, in June, 1956, three radio astronomers of the U.S. Naval Research Laboratory in Washington detected very weak radio waves from the planet

Venus. The men, Cornell H. Mayer, Russell M. Sloanaker, and Timothy P. McCullough, used a 50-foot radio telescope and special electronic equipment with a high radio frequency of 10,000 megacycles.

In September, 1956, the same trio first detected radio waves from Mars, measured at a wave length of three centimeters. They believe that these signals are related to the surface temperature of the planet, and after making more than fifty measurements the scientists concluded that Mars has an average temperature slightly lower than the freezing point of water.

In 1956 the radio telescope was aimed at the planet Jupiter, largest in our solar system, and early in 1957 the same three observers measured radiation signals originating on that planet. The Jupiter signals, twice as strong as those from Mars, indicated that Jupiter is a celestial freezer with a temperature of about 200 degrees below zero! Studies by the Navy scientists are continuing with the radio telescope.

A radio telescope is a saucer-shaped metal "ear," appropriately nicknamed "the dish." The aluminum dish of the Navy instrument which detected the signals from Mars, Venus and Jupiter, is 50 feet in diameter and stands on top of one building of the sprawling Naval Research Laboratory in Washington. It is mounted equatorially, in the same manner as an optical telescope would be, except that the mounting was originally a five-inch Navy gun mount which has been modified to accommodate the radio telescope.

The Naval Research Laboratory in 1957 built a radio telescope in southern Maryland, with a dish 84 feet across. This is slightly larger than an 82-foot instrument built by the Dutch and now in operation at The Hague, but it is a midget compared to a British radio telescope which has a dish measuring a tremendous 250 feet in diameter! This giant saucer, sixty-two feet deep and weighing some 600 tons, is mounted on two towers and pivots on a horizontal axis about 180 feet above the ground at Jodrell Bank, England.

The National Science Foundation of Washington is building a 140-foot radio telescope in Pocahontas County, West Virginia, which will be the biggest instrument of its kind in the United States. (This Foundation is also planning to finance the building of a new 80-inch reflecting telescope and observatory, probably to be located in Arizona, to be completed within the next few years.)

The discovery that celestial bodies transmitted radio waves was made accidentally by Karl G. Jansky of the Bell Telephone Laboratories in 1931. Jansky was trying to learn what caused a considerable amount of atmospheric interference with transoceanic radio-telephone operation. With his instruments he detected cosmic radio radiations on a frequency of 2.5 megacycles, which he believed were coming from the sun. Instead, he found that they came from the Milky Way.

Other technicians and institutions soon began to experiment with radio detection devices, and today many countries of the world are turning their metallic "ears" skyward to study the sun, moon, stars, nebulae, and interstellar dust and gases. The radio telescope can operate in fair weather or foul, unlike the optical telescope, which cannot penetrate clouds. The radio telescope can cover bands much greater than the wave lengths visible to the eye or the camera, which means that the radio astronomer can detect invisible objects in the heavens and can listen to the great dust or gaseous clouds of the Milky Way that once seemed like vast open spaces in the sky.

Celestial listening and even celestial gazing are not enough to satisfy modern man, for he is convinced that he can one day be shot from the earth into outer space, perhaps to the moon or a planet. There was a time when such a project would be labeled a fantasy, but the successful Russian launching of a man-made moon on October 4, 1957, brought the dream much closer to reality.

The Russian "moon," a globe 22 inches in diameter, weighing 184 pounds, was rocketed into an orbit about 560 miles above the earth's surface, where it whizzed through space at the terrific speed of almost 18,000 miles per hour. At this rate, it would take you *less than one minute* to travel from New York to Washington, or from Chicago to Detroit!

As this is written, the United States is preparing to shoot into the skies six or more artificial satellites which scientists hope will pick up and radio back new information about the mysteries of space. This earth satellite program, called "Project Vanguard," is an important part of the International Geophysical Year (ending December 31, 1958), during which some seventy nations are working together to gain new knowledge about our earth and its atmosphere. The world's leading geophysicists and scientific experts are making studies of geomagnetism, cosmic rays, meteorology, seismology, solar activity, ionospheric physics, glaciology, oceanography, aurora and airglow, latitudes and longitudes, gravity, and satellite observations.

The American artificial satellite is smaller than those first launched by the Russians. It is a metal sphere about 20 inches in diameter, weighing only twenty-one and a half pounds. About half of this weight is in batteries and instruments which will broadcast signals back to earth. The instruments are encased in plastic foam and contained in a cylinder in the center of the sphere. As in the case of the Russian "moon," one of the instruments is a transmitter which will make it possible to track the satellite by radio.

Dr. Richard W. Porter, Chairman of the U.S. National Committee for the International Geophysical Year, tells us something about this wonderful experiment.

"In order to create an artificial earth satellite," he said, "it is necessary to raise an object to an altitude where the air density is very small, and to make it go fast enough in a direction parallel to the earth's surface so that its centrifugal force, or the force tending to make it fly off into space, will be just equal to the gravitational force which tends to make it fall toward the center of the earth. The minimum altitude turns out to be about 200 miles and the velocity between 18,000 and 19,000 miles per hour. The very small amount of air which remains at this altitude will slow the satellite gradually, but it is believed that in such an orbit the satellite would persist for at least several weeks. At 300 miles it is believed that the satellite would possibly last for as long as a year and perhaps even longer."

The American satellite will be launched from Patrick Air Force Base on the east coast of Florida at Cape Canaveral, by a three-stage rocket assembly designed by the Glenn L. Martin Company, Baltimore, Maryland. The entire "bullet" will be about seventy feet long and forty-five inches in diameter, weighing about eleven tons.

The first rocket will start the entire assembly on its journey. When the first rocket's fuel is gone, some forty miles up, the assembly will be traveling between 3,000 and 4,000 miles per hour. The first stage will then drop into the ocean. The second stage will take over, boosting the speed to about 11,000 miles an hour, burning out and dropping off at an altitude of about 130 miles. The remaining part will coast upward, and when it reaches a height of about 300 miles the last rocket will shoot the satellite into its elliptical orbit at a speed of about 18,000 miles per hour—a speed calculated to counteract the pull of gravity from the earth. This was the estimated speed of the Russian satellite, which circled the earth about every ninety minutes. Gradually it will slow down and drop closer and closer to the earth, and when it enters the denser air at lower levels, friction will burn it up, like a shooting star.

What does science hope to gain by sending up this

man-made moon? "For the first time in history," Dr. Porter says, "man will have, in effect, a laboratory in space where, far above the dense and masking atmosphere, we can explore the nature of outer space, the nature of solar radiations, and the nature of particles in interplanetary space."

Mr. C. C. Furnas, Assistant Secretary of Defense, points out that the determination of the satellite's position with respect to time at different parts of the earth will be very important—and this is where telescopic observation plays a major role.

"Depending upon the reflectivity," Mr. Furnas explains, "the satellite will have a brightness of the order of a fifth- or sixth-magnitude star, and if the location is known exactly for a particular time under very clear atmospheric conditions, it might be observable with a good pair of binoculars. It should be very readily observable with a modest astronomical telescope if one knows approximately where to look for it. Twelve prime astronomical observatory stations are planned in different parts of the world with some 200 secondary stations, and it is hoped that many other nations and amateur groups may enter into this program of physical observation."

Hundreds of amateur astronomers in the United States are participating in "Operation Moonwatch"— a careful and systematic observation of the satellite with small telescopes designed for the purpose. Responsibility for this program was assigned by the National Academy of Sciences, through the National Science Foundation, to the Smithsonian Astrophysical Observatory.

Intermittently the Smithsonian Astrophysical Observatory sends out a *Bulletin for Visual Observers of Satellites*, as part of *Sky and Telescope* magazine, to keep amateur astronomers abreast of developments in the program.

"Primary objective of the visual program," say the Smithsonian people, "is to make sure that an observable satellite will not pass over a station without being observed with acceptable accuracy. Observing groups in any given geographical area will be informed when an observable satellite may be expected in their region. When a group leader is informed that during an approaching twilight period a satellite is expected to be observed from his station, he will have the responsibility of notifying members of his group and readying them for action."

Action is necessary during twilight morning or evening hours, because then the satellite will reflect sunlight and the observer will be in shadow.

The programmers believe that about thirty people can work effectively as a single observing team, and that a smaller group can do very useful work. Team members sit in a straight line, one behind the other, so arranged that their fields of view overlap. On a table before him, each has a telescope, preferably one designed especially for "Operation Moonwatch." This is a refractor in an aluminum tube 8½ inches long, 2⅜ inches in diameter. Immediately in front of the objective lens is a mirror, set at a 45-degree angle. Sighting into this mirror, the observer need not crane his neck, and may sit comfortably as he looks downward to see the satellite pass overhead.

The observers sit in a north-south direction "on the meridian," or line, which the artificial moon will cross in its east-to-west journey. (The Russian satellite traveled north and south.) Each observer is responsible for viewing a fixed patch of sky and must not move his instrument to try to track the satellite. Since the fields of view overlap it is expected that one or perhaps two will see the "moon" as it crosses the sky above the group, and the results of their observations should provide data of "acceptable accuracy."

To record this data the Smithsonian experts recommend that each group be equipped with a short-wave radio to obtain accurate time signals, and with a tape recorder or some other type of recording equipment, so that an immediate record may be made of time and other information. Stop watches or other timepieces measuring seconds will be indispensable.

There is one important DON'T which the program planners want to impress upon amateur astronomers: *Don't make "lone-wolf" reports of satellite observations!* That is, if you are an amateur astronomer and are not a member of an official satellite-observing team, don't send reports to the Smithsonian or others if you happen to see the satellite in your area. The reason for this is that each observing group will operate from a predetermined and exact geographical location, the position of which has been "fed" into the memory of the central computing machine. Reports of observations made by teams will be transmitted swiftly to the computing center—and any reports from areas other than those assigned to the official teams will be useless for scientific purposes.

If you want more information about the Visual Observers of Satellites, write to Mr. Leon Campbell, Jr., Smithsonian Astrophysical Observatory, 60 Garden Street, Cambridge 38, Massachusetts.

In addition to the amateur volunteer observers there will be a primary net of twelve international professional optical tracking stations, using improved Schmidt cameras and special "crystal clocks" readable to one millisecond, for precise timing of the satellite's observed positions. The twelve stations will be at White Sands, N. M.; Cocoa Beach, Fla.; Curaçao, Netherlands West Indies; Woomera, Australia; Tokyo, Japan; Cadiz, Spain; Arequipa, Peru; Naini-Tal, India; Villa Dolores, Argentina; Tehran or Shiraz, Iran; South Africa (probably Olifantsfontein); and Hawaii.

Several hours before the American satellite is due over each area, the latest data on its orbit will be radioed to the station, giving all available information including the moment when tracking must begin. It is estimated that each station will be able to photograph the satellite at least once a week, making between ten and one hundred separate photographs during each transit. All information and films will go to the computing center at Cambridge, Massachusetts, for use in improving predictions of the satellite's flight through space.

Radio tracking will also be important. The radio tracking system, known as Minitrack, will pick up radio signals transmitted by the satellite. If for any reason the satellite's radio transmitting equipment fails, then the optical tracking system assumes the greatest importance.

In watching the artificial moon and in listening to its radio "beeps" man learned more than he has ever known about outer space. He may build bigger satellites and eventually rocket ships which will carry passengers to the moon or planets. Whatever happens, we may be sure that man will continue to use and to improve the telescope and its wonderful offshoots—the microscope, the surveyor's transit, the binocular, the telescopic lens. Man has already seen marvels which defy the imagination. Today, through the lenses and mirrors of the telescope, he is actually looking into a whole new exciting era—the Age of Outer Space, truly the greatest show in sight.

Centuries ago, Johann Kepler, the friend of Tycho Brahe, summed it all up in twenty-nine words in a book called *The Dioptrice:*

"O, telescope, instrument of much knowledge,
more precious than any sceptre! Is not he
who holds thee in his hand made king and
lord of the works of God?"

SOME OF THE WORLD'S LARGEST TELESCOPES

Reflectors

200-inch California Institute of Technology, Mount Palomar, California.

120-inch Lick Observatory, Mount Hamilton, California.

100-inch Carnegie Institution, Mount Wilson, Pasadena, California.

96-inch University of Michigan Observatory, Ann Arbor, Michigan.

82-inch McDonald Observatory of the University of Texas, Mount Locke, Texas.

74-inch David Dunlap Observatory, University of Toronto, Toronto, Ontario.

72-inch Dominion Astrophysical Observatory, Victoria, B. C.

69-inch Perkins Observatory, Ohio Wesleyan University, Delaware, Ohio.

61-inch Harvard Observatory, Cambridge, Massachusetts.

60-inch Mount Wilson Observatory, Pasadena, California.

60-inch Harvard Observatory, Southern Station, Bloemfontein, Union of South Africa.

60-inch National Observatory of the Argentine Republic, Córdoba, Argentina.

48½-inch Berlin-Babelsburg Observatory, Berlin, Germany.

48-inch   Melbourne Observatory, Melbourne, Australia.
47-inch   St. Michel Observatory, Haute-Province, France.
42-inch   Lowell Observatory, Flagstaff, Arizona.
40-inch   U. S. Naval Observatory, Flagstaff, Arizona.
40-inch   Merate, Italy.
40-inch   Stockholm Observatory, Stockholm, Sweden.
40-inch   Simeis Observatory (Pulkowa), Crimea, U.S.S.R.

Refractors

40-inch   Yerkes Observatory, University of Chicago, Williams Bay, Wisconsin.
36-inch   Lick Observatory, Mount Hamilton, California.
32½-inch   Meudon Branch, Paris Observatory, Meudon, France.
31½-inch   Astrophysical Observatory, Potsdam, Germany.
30-inch   Pulkowa Observatory, Leningrad, U.S.S.R.
30-inch   Allegheny Observatory, University of Pittsburgh, Pittsburgh, Pennsylvania.
30-inch   University of Paris Observatory, Nice, France.
28-inch   Royal Observatory, East Sussex, England.
27-inch   University of Michigan, Southern Station, Bloemfontein, Union of South Africa.
27-inch   University Observatory, Vienna, Austria.
26½-inch   Union Observatory, Johannesburg, Union of South Africa.
26-inch   U. S. Naval Observatory, Washington, D. C.
26-inch   Leander McCormick Observatory, University of Virginia, Charlottesville, Va.
26-inch   Yale University Observatory, Southern Station, Johannesburg, Union of South Africa.
26-inch   Royal Observatory, East Sussex, England

SOURCES OF
FURTHER INFORMATION

American Association of Variable Star Observers
c/o Mrs. Margaret W. Mayall
4 Brattle Street
Cambridge, Mass.

American Museum-Hayden Planetarium
81st Street and Central Park West
New York 24, N. Y.

Association of Lunar and Planetary Observers
c/o Mr. Walter H. Haas
1203 N. Alameda Boulevard
Las Cruces, N. M.

Astronomical League
c/o Mrs. Wilma Cherup
4 Klopfer Street
Pittsburgh 9, Pa.

Astrophysical Observatory
Smithsonian Institution
Cambridge 38, Mass. (or Washington 25, D. C.)

Children's Museum
Fort Worth, Texas

Corning Glass Works
Corning, N. Y.

Harvard Observatory
Cambridge 38, Mass.

Lick Observatory
Mount Hamilton, California

Mount Wilson and Palomar Observatories
813 Santa Barbara Street
Pasadena, California

National Academy of Sciences
2101 Constitution Ave., N. W.
Washington, D. C.

National Science Foundation
1520 H Street, N. W.
Washington, D. C.

Royal Astronomical Society of Canada
c/o Mr. E. J. A. Kennedy
252 College Street
Toronto, Ontario, Canada

Spitz Laboratories
Yorklyn, Delaware

U. S. Naval Observatory
Washington 25, D. C.

U. S. Naval Research Laboratory
Washington 25, D. C.

Yerkes Observatory
Williams Bay, Wisconsin

SOME DEALERS IN TELESCOPES AND ACCESSORIES

(Write for catalogues and information)

Bausch & Lomb, Inc.,
635 St. Paul Street,
Rochester, N. Y. 14608   (Telescopes, lenses)

178

Cave Optical Company,
4137 East Anaheim Street,
Long Beach, Calif. 90804   (Telescopes and mirrors)

Criterion Manufacturing Co.
331 Church Street,
Hartford, Conn.   (Telescopes)

Edmund Scientific Company,
101 E. Gloucester Pike,
Barrington, N. J. 08007   (Telescopes and accessories)

Jaegers, A.,
The Glass House,
691 Merrick Road,
Lynbrook, N. Y. 11563   (Telescopes, mirrors, lenses)

Magnusson, Oscar
14570 West 52nd Avenue,   (Telescopes, mountings,
Arvada, Colo. 80002   drives)

Precision Optical Supply Co.,
P. O. Box, 99 Jerome Station,   (Telescope mirrors and sup-
New York, N. Y. 10468   plies)

Questar Corporation,
New Hope, Pa. 18938   (Telescopes, special cameras)

Ross, Harry
61 Reade Street,
New York, N. Y. 10007   (Telescopes, microscopes)

Spitz Laboratories, Inc.,
Yorklyn, Del. 19736   (Planetariums)

Telescopics,
6565 Romain Street,   (Amateur and professional
Los Angeles, Calif. 90038   telescope supplies)

BIBLIOGRAPHY

All About the Stars, by A. T. White. Random House, New York, 1954.

Amateur Telescope Making, edited by A. G. Ingalls. Scientific American Publishing Company, New York (3 vol.). (Vols. II and III are supplements to Vol. I, which teaches basic telescope-making).

Astronomy, by R. H. Baker. Van Nostrand, New York, 1955 (6th ed.).

Astronomy, by J. C. Duncan. Harper, New York, 1955 (5th ed.).

Astronomy Handbook, by Dr. Leon A. Hausman. Fawcett Publications, Inc., Greenwich, Conn., 1956.

Astronomy Made Simple, by Meir H. Degani. Garden City Books, New York, 1955.

Between the Planets, by F. G. Watson. Harvard University Press, Cambridge, Mass., 1956.

Boy Scientist, The, by John Lewellen. Simon & Schuster, New York, 1955.

Conquest of Space, The, by Willy Ley. Viking Press, New York, 1952.

Earth, Moon and Planets, by F. L. Whipple. Harvard University Press, Cambridge, Mass., 1941.

Earth Satellites, by Patrick Moore. Norton, New York, 1956.

Field Book of the Skies, by William T. Olcott. Putnam, New York, 1954.

Galileo, First Observer of Marvellous Things, by Elma Ehrlich Levinger. Julian Messner, Inc., New York, 1952.

George Ellery Hale, by Walter S. Adams. Reprinted from *Astrophysical Journal,* Vol. 87, 1938.

Glass and You. Corning Glass Works, Corning, N. Y., 1953.

Glass Giant of Palomar, The, by David O. Woodbury. Dodd, New York, 1953.

Going Into Space, by Arthur C. Clarke. Harper, New York, 1954.

Golden Book of Astronomy, The, by Rose Wyler and Gerald Ames. Simon & Schuster, New York, 1955.

Great Astronomers, The, by H. S. Williams. Simon & Schuster, New York, 1930.

Griffith Observer, The. A magazine published monthly by The Griffith Observatory, Los Angeles, California.

Guide to the Constellations, by S. G. Barton and W. H. Barton. McGraw-Hill, New York, 1943 (3rd ed.).

Handbook of the Heavens, by Hubert J. Bernhard, Dorothy A. Bennett, and Hugh S. Rice. McGraw, New York, 1948.

History of Astronomy, The, by Giorgio Abetti. Henry Schuman, New York, 1952.

History of the Telescope, The, by Henry C. King. Sky Publishing Company, Cambridge, Mass., 1955.

How to Make and Use a Telescope, by H. Percy Wilkins and Patrick Moore. Norton, New York, 1956.

John Alfred Brashear, The Autobiography of a Man Who Loved the Stars. The American Society of Mechanical Engineers, New York, 1924.

Making Your Own Telescope, by A. J. Thompson. Sky Publishing Corporation, Cambridge, Mass.

Men, Mirrors and Stars, by G. Edward Pendray. Harper, New York, 1946.

Observers' Handbook (annual). Royal Astronomical Society of Canada, Toronto, Ontario.

Observing the Heavens, by Peter Hood. Oxford University Press, New York, 1955.

Palomar, by Helen Wright. Macmillan, New York, 1952.

Photographic Giants of Palomar, by J. S. Fassero and R. W. Porter. Westernlore Press, 1947.

Photography in Astronomy, by E. W. H. Selwyn. Eastman Kodak Company, Rochester, N. Y., 1950.

Pictorial Astronomy, by D. Alter and C. H. Cleminshaw. Crowell, New York, 1952.

Popular Guide to the Heavens, by Sir Robert S. Ball. George Philip and Son, London, 1955 (5th ed.).

Prism and Lens Making, by F. Twyman. Hilger & Watts, London, 1952 (2nd ed.).

Radio Astronomy, by Bernard Lovell and J. A. Clegg. Wiley, New York, 1952.

Reports of Director of the Solar Observatory, Mount Wilson, California, by George E. Hale. (Annual reports to Carnegie Institution, 1905-1915).

Science and Imagination, by Marjorie Nicolson. Cornell University Press, Ithaca, N. Y., 1956.

Signals From the Stars, by George Ellery Hale. Scribner, New York and London, 1931.

Sky and Telescope (monthly magazine). Sky Publishing Corporation, Cambridge, Mass.

Sky Reporter, The, (monthly pamphlet). American Museum-Hayden Planetarium, New York.

Skyshooting: Hunting the Stars With Your Camera, by R. N. and M. L. W. Mayall. Ronald Press, New York, 1949.

Stars and Men, by Stephen Ionides. Bobbs-Merrill, Indianapolis, Ind., 1939.

Stories of Great Astronomers, by Edward S. Holden. D. Appleton & Company, New York and London, 1912.

Story of Astronomy, The, by A. L. Draper and M. Lockwood. Dial Press, New York, 1939.

Story of the Telescope, The, by Arthur Mee. Published by the author at Llanishen, Cardiff, 1909.

Telescope, The, by Louis Bell. McGraw-Hill, New York, 1922.

Telescopes and Accessories, by G. Z. Dimitroff and J. G. Baker. Harvard University Press, Cambridge, Mass., 1945.

Ten Years' Work of a Mountain Observatory, by George Ellery Hale. Carnegie Institution, Washington, D. C., 1915.

Theory of the Microscope, by James R. Benford (booklet). Bausch & Lomb Optical Company, Rochester 2, N. Y., 1955.

Torch-Bearers, The, by Alfred Noyes. W. Blackwood and Sons, London, 1922.

Tycho Brahe, by J. L. E. Dreyer. A. and C. Black, Edinburgh, 1890.

When the Stars Come Out, by R. H. Baker. Viking Press, New York (revised 1954).

(Note: Interesting articles on "Astronomy" and "Telescope" are published in the Encyclopedia Americana, Encyclopedia Britannica, The World Book Encyclopedia, and other standard reference works).

INDEX

Aberration, chromatic, 25, 34, 41, 45, 56
Aberration of light, 38
Aberration, spherical, 41, 45, 46
Accessories, dealers in telescopes and, 157-161, 178-181
Achromatic eyepiece, 34, 41
Achromatic lens, 57, 65
Adams, Walter S., 117
"Aerial telescopes," 35-41
Aircraft, Langley's, 77
Allegheny Observatory, 70, 73, 75
Allegheny Telescope Association, 73
Allen Academy, Chicago, 110
Alpha Lyrae, first photograph of, 85
Altazimuth mounting, 81
Alvan Clark and Sons (see *Clark*), 65, 68, 77
Amateur astronomers, 138-163
American Academy of Arts and Sciences, 143
American Association of Variable Star Observers, 141
American Journal of Science and Art, The, 76
American Meteor Society, 144
American Museum-Hayden Planetarium, 55
American Optical Company, 73
Annealing, 200-inch mirror, 128
Archer, Scott, 86
Aristotle, 23
Armati, Salvino d'Armato degli, 20
Artificial moon, 167
Association of Lunar and Planetary Observers, 145
Astigmatism, overcoming, in photography, 94
Astrograph, 20-inch, at Lick Observatory, 106
Astronomer Royal, Edmund Halley as, 40
Astronomer, The, epitaph from, 73
Astronomical League, The, 146
Astronomical library, Lick Observatory, 107
Atlas, sky, 135

Auzout, Adrien, 36

Bacon, Roger, 20
Barnard, Edward E., 104
Bass, George, 57
Battle of Marston Moor, 40
Baum, Dr. W. A., 93
Baustian, W. W., 106
"Bell metal," use of, for mirrors, 44, 64
Bell Telephone Laboratories, 166
Beloit College, 80
Berlin, University of, 111
Bibliography, 182-185
Bille, Steene, 15
Bolton, W. B., 86
Bond, George, 85
Bond, George P., 88
Bond, William Cranch, 85
Bradley, James, 37
Brahe, Tycho, 13-19, 41, 174
Brashear, John Alfred, 68-73, 113
Brashear, Phoebe, 69
Brasseuir, family name of Brashear, 68
Brown, Marcus H., 133
"Brownie" box camera, first, 87
Bunsen, Robert W., 90
Bureau of Standards, National, 78, 139
Burlington Railroad, 131
Burnham, S. W., 101

California Institute of Technology, 106, 132, 135, 140
California School of Mechanic Arts, The, 99
California, University of, 99
Calotype process, 84, 86
Camera obscura, 83
Camera, use of, in observatories, 83
Campbell, Leon, Jr., 173
Canada, Royal Astronomical Society of, 147
Canterbury, Archbishop of, 54
Carnegie, Andrew, 115
Carnegie Corporation, 106

185

Carnegie Institution of Washington, 93, 114, 135
Cassegrain, Guillaume (William), 46
Cassiopeia, constellation of, 16
"Castle of the Stars," 17
Cave Optical Company, 159, 179
Cheops, Pyramid of, 99
Cherup, Mrs. Wilma, 146
Chicago, University of, 110
Children's Museum, Fort Worth, 149
Chromatic aberration, 25, 34, 41, 45, 56
Clark, Alvan, 62-68, 78, 90, 111
Clark, Alvan, and Sons, 77, 103
Clark, Alvan G., 65, 103
Clark, George Bassett, 64
Clock, Sir William Herschel's giant, 55
Coast Instrument, Inc., 159, 179
Coma, combatting, in photography, 94
Comet, derivation of word, 41
    Donati's, 73
    Wild, 144
Comets, hunting for, 142
    study of, by Barnard, 104
    by Halley, 40
Common, A. A., 105
Conklin, Miss Evalina, 110
Copernicus, Nicolaus, 27
Corning Glass Works, 124-133
Coudé focus, 120-inch reflector, 107
Criterion Manufacturing Company, 158-9, 179
Crossley, Edward, 105
Crown glass, 56

Daguerre, Louis Jacques Mandé, 82, 84
Daguerreotype, 82, 84-86
Dark nebulae, 104
Davis, Kenneth W., 151
Davy, Sir Humphry, 83
Dawes, Rev. W. R., 66
Dean, Professor Philotus, 74, 76
Declination axis, 81
de la Rue, Warren, 88
Demisiani, Johann, 24
Dioptrice, The, 174
Discover the Stars, 159
Dollond, John and Peter, 57-58
Donati, Giovanni Battista, 73

Donati's Comet, 73
Double stars, detection of, by Clark, 67
    Herschel's study of, 53
Draper, Dr. Henry, 70, 102
Draper, Dr. John W., 85

Eastman Dry Plate and Film Company, 87
Eastman, George, 86
Eastman Kodak Company, 87
Edinburgh, University of, 49
Edison, Thomas, 125
Edmund Scientific Company, 157, 179
Edscorp Satellite Telescope, 158
Emperor Rudolph II, 17
Equatorial mounting, 81-82
Eye, human, absence of chromatic aberration in, 56

Fecker, Gottlieb L., 73
Fecker, J. W., 73
Fecker, J. W., Inc., 73, 161, 179
"Figuring," shaping of mirrors known as, 44
Fitz of New York, 74
Fizeau, Armand, 85
Flint glass, 56
Floor, movable, at Lick Observatory, 103
Floyd, Capt. R. S., 101
Floyd, Oliver, 160
"Fortress of the Heavens," 16
Fosdick, Dr. Raymond B., 136
Foucault, Jean Bernard Léon, 48, 62, 85
Fraser, Thomas E., 100
Fraunhofer, Joseph von, 59, 65, 89
"Fraunhofer lines," 90
Furnas, C. C., 170

Galilei, Galileo, 22-31, 79
Galilei, Vincenzio, 23
Gamma Draconis (star), 37
Gascoigne, William, 39
Gelatine emulsion, use of, in photography, 86, 91
Georgium Sidus, planet, 53
Glass, composition of, 124
    optical, used by Alvan Clark, 66
    Pyrex, for 200-inch mirror, 126
    types of, 125
Glasses (spectacles), 20

Graham, George, 37
Gravitation, Law of, Newton's, 46
Great Nebula of Orion, 35, 52
Greenwich meridian, 79
Greenwich Observatory, 89
Gregorian telescope, diagram of, 43
  Herschel's experience with, 51
Gregory, James, 42
Gross, Kay, 150
Guinand, Pierre Louis, 58
Gutenberg, Johann, 21
Gyroscope, invention of the, 62

Haas, Walter H., 146
Hadley, George/Henry/John, 48
Hainzel, John and Paul, 14
Hale, George Ellery, 108-123, 133, 135, 139
"Hale Telescope, The," 123, 125
Hall, Chester Moor, 56
Hall, Dr. John S., 93, 94
Halley, Edmund, 40
"Halley's Comet," 40
Harper, W. R., 111
Hartness, James, 139
Harvard Observatory, 62, 65, 77, 85, 142
Harvard University, 162
Heliostat, 114
Herschel, Alexander, 49, 51
Herschel, Caroline, 49-56
Herschel, Friedrich Wilhelm, 49-56
Herschel, John, 55
Herschel, Sir William, 49-56
Hevelius, Elizabeth, 36
Hevelius, Johann, 35
Hiskey, Joseph, 97
Hoene, Island of, 16
Holden, Edward S., 100, 101
Home for Old Ladies, San Francisco, 99
Hooke, Robert, 37
Hooker, John D., 115
Hooker Telescope, 100-inch, 117, 125
Hudson Pacific-Murphy Corporation, 106
Huggins, William, 90
Hussey, Professor W. J., 114
Huygens, Christiaan, 32-36, 40, 41, 48
Hveen, Island of, 16

Image amplifier, development of, 92, 93
Image multiplier, 92, 93
Information, sources of further, 177-178
Ingalls, Albert G., 139, 140
Inquisition, Galileo and the, 29
International Geophysical Year, 167

Jansky, Karl G., 166
Janssen, Hans and Zacharias, 22
Johnson, Gaylord, 159
Joint Committee on Image Tubes for Telescopes, 93
Jones and Lamson Machine Company, 139
Jupiter, moons of, 26
  radio waves from, 165

Kalakaua, King, 102
Kansas, University of, 148
Keeler, James Edward, 73, 105
Kennedy, E. J. A., 147
Kenwood Observatory, 110
Kepler, Johann, 17, 28, 30, 174
"Kepler's Laws," 31, 46
Kew Observatory, 88
Key, Francis Scott, 99
King Christian IV of Denmark, 17
King Frederick II of Denmark, 16, 17
Kirchhoff, Gustav Robert, 90
Kodak camera, origin of, 87
Kodak Research Laboratories, 87
Krewalk, John J., 159

Langley, Dr. Samuel Pierpont, 70, 72, 75-77
Lens, achromatic, 57
  Dollond achromatic (diagram), 58
  origin of word, 20
  plano-concave, plano-convex, 21
  theft of, from Allegheny Observatory, 76
Lenses, disks for, made by Guinand, 59
  study of, by Alvan Clark, 65
Lentil, similarity of, to lens shape, 20
"Leviathan of Parsonstown, The," 61
Library, telescope lending, 149
Lichtman, Philip, 162
"Lick House, The," 98

Lick, James, 97-100, 108
Lick Observatory, 96-108, 110, 114
Liebig, Justus von, 62
Light, aberration of, 38
  refraction of, 38, 56
  velocity of, 62
  zodiacal, study of, 145
Light year, defined, 120
Lippersheim, Hans, 21
Lippershey, Hans, 21
Longines Wittnauer Watch Company, 56
Lowell, Dr. Percival, 148
Lowell Observatory, 148
Lunar and Planetary Observers, Association of, 145

Mantois, glass made by, 111
Marion, Walter, 146
Mars, study of, by Clyde Tombaugh, 148
  radio waves from, 165
Martin, Glenn L., Company, 169
Massachusetts Institute of Technology, 110, 138
Mayall, Mrs. Margaret W., 141
Mayer, Cornell H., 165
McCauley, Dr. George V., 126
McCullough, Timothy P., 165
McDowell, James B., 72
Meridian, description of, 76
  Zero (Greenwich), 79
Metius, James, 22
Meteors, observation of, 144
Micrometer, filar, invention of, 39
Milky Way galaxy, 106
  radio signals from, 166
  study of, through 100-inch telescope, 119
Miller, Professor W. A., 90
Minitrack, 174
Mirror, aluminized, at Lick Observatory, 106
  Hooker Telescope 100-inch, 116
  Mount Palomar 200-inch, 125
  silvering of, by Brashear, 71
Mirrors, metal, polishing of, by Hadley, 48
  silvering of, 62
  test for curvature of, 48
Mitchell, Maria, 142-3
Molyneux, Samuel, 37
Moon, amateur studies of, 145
  Draper photographs the, 85

Russian artificial, 167
Morse, Samuel F. B., 85
Mount Hamilton, 100, 107
Mount Palomar Observatory, 93, 123-137
Mount Wilson Observatory, 114-122
Mounting, altazimuth telescope, 81
  built by Earl of Rosse, 61
  equatorial, 81-82
  Hale 200-inch telescope, 134

National Academy of Sciences, 170
National Capital Astronomers Club, 163
National Geographic Society, 135
National Observatory, Paris, 79
National Science Foundation, 166, 170
Naval Observatory, U. S., 76-78, 80, 93
Naval Radio Station, time signals from, 78
Naval Research Laboratory, U. S., 164
Neal "one-buck telescope," diagram of, 155
Nebulae, photographs of, 105
New York Central Railroad, 130
Newcomb, Professor Simon, 101
Newton, Sir Isaac, 43, 45, 64, 89, 101
Niepce, J. N., 82, 84
Noble, Miss Charlie M., 149-151
North Carolina, University of, 77
Noyes, Alfred, 117

Observatory, Lick, 97-108
  Mount Palomar, 123-137
  Mount Wilson, 114-122
  Yerkes, 108-114
Obsidian, primitive use of, 124
Occultations, star, study of, 144
Octagon Chapel, 49
Olivier, Charles P., 144
"Operation Moonwatch," 153, 170
Opticians, union of, 42
Opus Majus, 20
Ornithologists, telescopes used by, 147

Padua, University of, 23
Paper, sensitized, 86
Paraboloid, described, 44
  mirrors, testing of, 62

Parsons, William, 60
Parsonstown, Ireland, 60
Patrick Air Force Base, 169
Peary, Admiral, 138
Pease, F. G., 136
Pease, Maria, 63
Photograph, first star, 85
Photographic Zenith Tubes (PZT), 78
Photographs, amateur astronomical, 162
  astronomical, by George Ritchey, 113
  astronomical, coma and astigmatism in, 94
  astronomical, improved by image amplifier, 92, 93
  equatorial mounting needed for astronomical, 81
  first spectroscopic, 91
  star, to determine time, 78
Photography, beginnings of, 83
Photography in Astronomy, 87
Photoheliograph, invention of, 88
Pierce, John M., 160, 180
Pisa, University of, 23
Pittsburgh, University of, 73
Planetarium, Charlie M. Noble, 151
  first, 152
  Spitz Junior, 159
Planetary motion, secret of, 46
Planets, difficulty in photographing, 93
  study of the, 145
Pluto, discovery of planet, 148
Polar axis, 81
Polo, Marco, 20
Pope Paul V, 28
Popular Astronomy, 139
Porter, Dr. Richard W., 168
Porter, Russell W., 137-140
Possibilities of Large Telescopes, The, 122
Power, telescope, 160
Pratt and Whitney Company, 80
Prime focus, 120-inch reflector, 107
Prism, use of, by Newton, 89
Pulkowa Observatory, 67
Pyrex glass, use of, for 200-inch mirror, 126

Quadrant, Tycho Brahe's, 14

Reflecting telescope (see *Telescope*)

Refracting telescope (see *Telescope*)
Refraction of light, 38, 56
Ritchey, George Willis, 113, 115, 117
Rockefeller General Education Board, 122
  International Education Board, 122
  Foundation, 122
Ross, Harry, 159, 180
Rosse, Earl of, 60
Royal Astronomical Society of Canada, 147
Royal Observatory, East Sussex, 79
Royal Society of London for Improving Practical Knowledge, 45, 88
Rudolphine Tables, 18, 19

St. Gobain Glass Works, 116
Santa Fe Railroad, 131
Satellite, artificial, 167
Saturn, ring around, 32
Sayce, B. J., 86
Schmidt, Bernhard, 95, 96
Schmidt, Camera, 96, 135, **173**
Schwarzschild, Conrad, 94
Scientific American, 139
Selwyn, E. W. H., 87
Sextant, 48
Short, James, 49
Sidus, Georgium, planet, 53
"Sign of the Golden Spectacles and Sea Quadrant," 58
Silhouette, photographic, 83
Silvering process, 62, 71
Simms, W. H., 89
Sky and Telescope, 146, 147
"Skyscope," 149
Slipher, Dr. E. C., 148
Sloanaker, Russell M., 165
Smithsonian Astrophysical Observatory, 171
Smithsonian Institution, 77
Solar photographs, de la Rue's, 88
Solar system, our, 120
Spectacles, early, 20
Spectrograph, origin of the, 91
Spectroheliograph, 91, 92, 114
Spectroscope, Hale's first use of, 110
  Newton's, 89
  Yerkes Observatory, 113
Spectrum, 89, 113
Speculum, reflector called, 44

Spherical aberration, 41, 45-6
Spitz, Armand N., 151-153
Spitz Junior Planetarium, 159
Spitz Laboratories, 153
Stadius, John, 14
Standards, National Bureau of, 78, 139
Star, first photograph of, 85
first spectroscopic analysis of, 90
occultations, study of, 144
photographs, determining time by, 78
Star-Spangled Banner, The, 99
Stellafane, 139, 160
Sternglass, Dr. E. J., 92
Stjerneborg (observatory), 17
Strolling Astronomer, The, 146
Struve, Dr. Friedrich Georg Wilhelm, 67
Studies in Spectrum Analysis, Lockyer's, 110
Sun, da la Rue's photographs of, 88
Sunspots, analysis of, 91
counting of, 141
drawings of, by Langley, 75
Swasey, Ambrose, 80, 102, 106, 111-112

Tabulae Bergenses, 13
Talbot, William Henry Fox, 83
"Talbotype" process, 84
Target-shooting, telescopes used in, 147
Tauchmann reflector, 107
Telescope, aerial, 35-41
Cassegrain's (diagram), 47
Galileo's, 24-26
Gregory's, 42-43
Hadley's, 48
Hale 200-inch, 125-137
Hooker 100-inch, 119, 121
how to make a simple, 154
Huygen's (diagram), 34
Kepler's (diagram), 30
Lick Observatory, 97-108
measurements with the, 39
Mount Palomar 200-inch, 124-137
Mount Wilson 100-inch, 115
Newton's (diagram), 45
origin of word, 24
Parsons' giant, 60
radio, 164-166
reflecting, 12, 42-62, 95
refracting, 22, 34, 42, 111

Yerkes Observatory 40-inch, 111
Telescopes, dealers in, 157-161, 178-181
Telescopic sight, invention of the, 39
Ten Years' Work of a Mountain Observatory, 120
Thaw, William, 72
Time, determination of, at Naval Observatory, 78
Time signals, first use of, 76
source of, 78
Titan, discovery of, 33
Tombaugh, Clyde, 148
"Tycho's Star," 16

"Uncle John" Brashear, 72
Union Iron Works, San Francisco, 102
United Scientific Company, 158, 181
Unitron Instrument Division, 158, 181
University of Chicago, Yerkes Observatory, 108-114
Uraniborg (observatory), 16
Uranus, planet, discovery of, 53

Vanderbilt University, 104
Vanguard, Project, 167
Variable stars, observation of, 141, 105
Vassar College, 143
Vassar, Matthew, 143
Venus, diameter of, 37
radio waves from, 165
von Fraunhofer, Joseph (see Fraunhofer), 59
von Liebig, Justus, 62

Wachtel, Milton M., 92
Walker, William H., 86
Wampler, Squire, 68
Warner and Swasey, 102, 106, 111-112
Warner and Swasey Observatory, 80
Warner, Worcester Reed, 80
Washington Monument, 36
Watchers of the Sky, The, 119
Wedgwood, Thomas, 83
Western Astronomers Association, 146

190

Western University of Pennsylvania, 75

Westinghouse Research Laboratories, 92

Wet Collodion plates, 90
process, 86

Whipple, J. A., 85

Wild, Paul, 144

Williams College, observatory at, 77

Wollaston, William H., 89

Yerkes, Charles T., 111

Yerkes Observatory, 108-114

Zeiss, Carl, Optical Company, 152

Zenith, described, 76

Ziegler polar expedition, 138

Zodiacal light, study of, 145

About the Author

HARRY EDWARD NEAL was born May 4, 1906 in Pittsfield, Massachusetts, but left there in 1925 to work for the Federal government as a stenographer. In 1957 he retired as Assistant Chief of the U. S. Secret Service to devote all of his time to free-lance writing. Before his retirement he wrote magazine articles and short stories which appeared in many national magazines. Today he concentrates on the writing of both juvenile and adult books, though occasionally he produces magazine pieces as well.